TRANSPORTATION

IN
THE WORLD
OF
THE FUTURE

TRANSP

ORTATION
IN
THE WORLD
OF
THE FUTURE

BY

HAL HELLMAN

PUBLISHED BY

M. Evans and Company, Inc. NEW YORK

AND DISTRIBUTED IN ASSOCIATION WITH

J. B. Lippincott Company

PHILADELPHIA AND NEW YORK

IN MEMORY OF

Julius Robley Almer

The list of people who have contributed time, information or material
to this book is a long one, and the author regrets that it is not possible
to thank all of them here. He would, however, like to acknowledge the
assistance provided by the following: Prof. J. V. Foa of Rensselaer Polytechnic Institute, Mr. Bruce J. Firkins of General Electric, Prof. R. J.
Hanson of M.I.T., Mr. Leon Katz of the Port of New York Authority,
and, most particularly, Mr. Myron Miller, Senior Engineer at the U.S.
Department of Transportation's Office of High Speed Transportation. Mr.
Miller provided much useful information and was kind enough to review
the manuscript as well. His comments were very useful.

H.H.

Contents

Prologue 3

1. Today's World of Transportation 7
2. Rail Rapid Transit 20
3. High Speed Ground Transportation 38
4. Tunnels and Tubes 59
5. The Road Ahead 76
6. The Electric Car and the City Center 92
7. Road/Rail Systems 112
8. Above and Below the Sea 129
9. Aircraft—Up and Away 146

Epilogue 172
Bibliography 177
Index 182

Prologue

ON HIS WAY into the kitchen, Andrew Mann touched the "Car" button on the electronic communications panel in the living room. By the time he had finished breakfast a rented Electra-car, delivered automatically from the town depot, was waiting for him at the door.

Andrew slid into the sleek two-seater, inserted his All-Credit card (which acted as both ignition key and accounting agent), stepped on the accelerator, and was on his way.

A short, two-mile drive brought him to the electronic highway. As he approached the entrance, he punched out his destination on the dashboard console, which automatically beamed the information, plus the car code, to the highway control computer.

Immediately, the computer announced via his car radio, "Sorry, Mr. Mann, but you will have to wait about two minutes before you can get onto the Autoway. We have just reached critical density. However, if you will drive onto the ramp at your right, you can relinquish manual control; the automatic system will take over and will check out your car at the same time.

"I see," continued Highway Control, "that you are going to the Long Distance Transportation Terminal in New York. Since traffic is particularly heavy this morning, some of the vehicles are being routed through the new Hudson Tunnel. Your distance to the terminal is therefore 28 miles; the trip will take 17 minutes. We will inform you when you are approaching your destination. Please switch to automatic now."

Andrew Mann flicked the proper switch and relaxed. "Now for an important decision," he chuckled. "Shall I read, sleep, or watch the news . . . ?"

Andrew opened his eyes. He could feel the car decelerating smoothly but perceptibly. His car radio came on and a gentle voice said, "Mr. Mann, you are approaching the terminal. We hope you enjoyed your ride. Thank you."

Andrew shook himself slightly and mumbled, "So soon?" He checked his cathode ray tube map display. Sure enough, the little white dot showed that he was entering the midtown New York area. "Hm. Must have slept right through the ride."

The Electra-car, still moving at a rapid clip, entered the new Hudson Tunnel and a moment later came to a smooth halt in the basement of the giant Long Distance Terminal. Andrew got out, punched the "Park" button, and watched the car glide off—to be used by someone else. He mused, "Seems to me I read somewhere that people had to park their own cars a hundred years ago. Seems hard to believe."

A few steps brought him to the glidewalk. He stepped on and a lovely female voice sounded in his ear. "Welcome, traveler, to the first fully integrated public transportation system on earth. Where are you bound?"

"Area 303, Oakland, California."

"Oh, I'm sorry, but the hypersonic transport has just left, and there won't be another one for two hours."

"That's all right. I'm in no rush and I would like to use the 'Tube' anyway. I've never used it before."

"Fine. The next train comes through from Boston in twenty-five minutes. A pod is waiting, however, in the subterminal. Unless you have some other need, I suggest you get off the glidewalk at Exit 2, which you will reach in a few moments. You will see the pod off to the right of the Exit sign. How much luggage do you have with you?"

"Just a hand case. I can handle it."

"Good. Do you have your All-Credit card with you?"

"Yes."

"Would you please show it to the accounting machine on your right?"

Andrew flashed his card, and the computer's voice continued, "Thank you. We'll charge your travel account at the end of the month. Will that be satisfactory?"

"Yes, that's fine."

"As you probably know, the main train does not stop as it comes through. The pod will be accelerated to the same speed as the main section and will then hook onto it. The train travels at roughly 1,000 miles per hour. Therefore, your trip will take just under three hours, and will bring you into the San Francisco terminal at 9:17 A.M. local time."

Andrew grinned and glanced at his watch. It read 9:25.

"At the terminal," his guide continued, "you have a choice of transportation modes. Are you perhaps going to the new two-mile-high building in Oakland?"

"Why, yes. I am."

"Well, in that case you could use the new Ele-Car, which would take you directly from the terminal to the building and then up to the floor of your choice. Or, since you are not in a great hurry and might like to get up above ground for a while, we would suggest that you take the Air-Cushion

Vehicle. It leaves directly from the terminal, crosses the bay and continues right into Oakland. It's a beautiful ride. The ACV then connects with a mini-bus that will take you to your destination. However, the total trip may be lengthened by ten minutes or so."

"That's all right. The air-cushion mode sounds like a good idea."

"Very well, then. When you get off at the San Francisco terminal, take the escalator marked 'ACV.' Incidentally, don't worry about the details. You will receive printed instructions on the train. All right, step off here, please."

Andrew stepped off sideways onto a belt that was moving in the same direction as he was, but more slowly, and then finally onto solid ground. He walked toward the pod, a sleek silver train-car—without windows.

His unseen companion anticipated his question. "Although there are no windows in the train, a large 3-D screen will show highlights of the areas through which you will be passing on your cross-country trip. There are also small screens and ear-pieces which will provide a wide choice of private entertainment; they may be used for long-distance calls, if you wish. For your further convenience, an autobarber, a snack bar, and a dictatyper are also available. If you need anything else, please ring. There is a hostess on board who will be happy to serve you. Goodbye now."

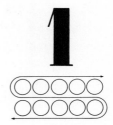

Today's World
of Transportation

THAT WAS quite a vision, wasn't it? Oddly enough, while a
great deal of what went on during Mr. Mann's trip sounds very
"far-out," none of it is impossible. There is nothing which
controverts the laws of nature (as we know them today), such
as anti-gravity or movement through time.

You may not believe this, but of all the items mentioned the
one that will be most difficult to achieve will be the one that
you probably didn't pay any attention to at all. I refer to the
phrase used by Mr. Mann's guide and "companion," namely
". . . the first fully integrated public transportation system
on earth."

Today, when a man takes a trip, he may have to contend with auto traffic, a bus system, a subway system, a train system, an airline, and perhaps even a ship or ferry. Rarely do the employees of one of these systems have any idea of what the others are doing by way of schedules or prices, and still less often do they care. What information they do have stems more from feelings of competition than of cooperation or aid to the passenger.

One disgusted traveler put it this way: "We in the United States have the greatest transportation system in the world today. The only ones who disagree are those who have tried to use it."

In truth, we do not have *a* transportation system. We have many. Sometimes they meet. Sometimes they almost meet. And sometimes they are on opposite sides of a city.

So there are two parts to the problem. One is the actual movement of people and goods. The other is the transfer process from one system to another. Transferees can expect little help in the process. Most travelers from city to city, or even from one section of a city to another, find they are quite on their own. Many a weary and puzzled traveler (not to mention commuter) would be thankful to have even a small part of our dream come true.

Can it? This is one of the questions we will explore in this book. Another question is: how far are we from that millenium? A third is concerned with what is being done now which will (or may) make that dream come true.

Transportation and the City

Before we go into these questions more carefully, we should look a little bit at the world of transportation, including city transportation, as it exists today. We start off with a fact that may surprise you, as it did me. The average American family spends fully 13 per cent of its income on transportation—for work, education, recreation, and social purposes. In some cities, such as Los Angeles and Detroit, the figure is more like 18 per cent. And as a nation, when we include industry, the proportion rises to a full 20 per cent, one-fifth of our Gross National Product. That's well over $160 billion just to move ourselves and our goods. President Johnson referred to transportation as the nation's largest industry.

About half the amount spent goes into the movement of goods. Indeed, the average city-dweller consumes some 18 *tons* of material annually. Every bit of it must be brought in from the outside. For, in contrast to farm and forest dwellers, city people cannot supply themselves with food, clothing, and shelter.

More and more, the major product of cities is ideas, or intelligence. It is in cities like New York, London, and Paris that headquarters for banking, insurance, publishing, advertising, finance, radio and television industries are found.

There are some who say that the city is doomed, that improvements in communications and transportation make it less necessary to concentrate in small areas than before. They say, furthermore, that increasing congestion is making it harder for commerce and industry to operate in crowded downtown areas, causing these businesses to flee to the suburbs. New York is pointed to as a prime example.

9

Yet, since World War II, more new office space has been built in New York City than *exists* in any other city in the world. One can hardly call this dying. What has happened, however, is more clearly seen in the residential areas. Here, it is true that downtown areas are either losing population or barely holding their own, while the surrounding areas—the suburbs—are truly exploding.

Is this coincidence? Did it just happen to happen now? No, the forces at work in city and suburb have been strongly influenced by developments in transportation. In other words, transportation is not merely a set of devices or a means for moving vehicles from one place to another. It is a basic force in shaping the course of our lives. It has been said that the history of civilization might be described as the history of transportation.

For centuries, until the early 1800's, travel was limited to foot and horse. The worker, and his boss, therefore, were both limited to living no more than about two or three miles—a comfortable commuting distance—from the center of a city, where most employment took place. Hence cities were quite limited in size, normally covering no more than about twenty square miles, but contained a highly dense population.

As recently as a century ago, one could see streams of walkers two and three miles long converging on the central area of London. In the 1890's, a thousand horse-buses were carrying over 100 million passengers per year into that city.

But change was in the air. Development in the late 1800's of the streetcar (or trolley), the railroad and rapid transit system (for example, the subway and "elevated") expanded the radius of urban movement to about five miles; the urban area (city plus suburbs) then covered perhaps eighty square miles.

The working-class suburbs of Chicago, Boston, and Philadelphia were literally created around the turn of the century by the newly built street-railway systems which radiated out from the city centers. In 1900, the most densely populated residential area of Manhattan, the East Side, contained almost half a million people in its most crowded square mile; today, thanks largely to the development of the city's rapid transit system, no square mile in the area now has more than 200,000 residents. In other words, the improved transport systems allowed increasing numbers of workers to live outside of the Central Business District (CBD) where most of them worked.

With the development of the automobile, the commuting radius expanded to 25 miles and even further. Urban areas now cover upwards of 2,000 square miles—one hundred times larger than the largest city of former times. Unfortunately, the poor cannot afford autos; they are pretty well restricted to living in or very close to the city centers.

The Modern Megalopolis

The expansion continues. Each year, urban America spreads at the rate of a million acres—an area as large as the state of Rhode Island. Today, over two-thirds of all Americans live in one of the great metropolitan areas such as New York, Chicago, or Los Angeles. By 1980, more than three out of four will be living in and around such cities.

One forecaster has predicted that by 1986 some cities in

11

India may have populations of 36 million! The New York metropolitan region already has about 17 million residents— more than the combined populations of fourteen other states.

Indeed, by 1980 the metropolitan areas will have expanded so greatly that many of the larger metropolises will begin to meet and merge into what has been named a *megalopolis*. (This word is from the Greek and means "great city." There actually was a city called Megalopolis in ancient Greece!)

By that year of 1980, half of all Americans will be crammed into just three such areas. One has been dubbed "Bosnywash," and refers to the northeast corridor stretching from Boston to Washington and including Providence, New Haven, New York, Philadelphia, and Baltimore (see map). Another is "Chipitt," named for Chicago and Pittsburgh, which will encompass cities in the Great Lakes area. The third, "Sansan," stretches along the Pacific Coast from San Francisco down to San Diego.

This large-scale concentration of people and resources has been made possible by improved transportation. The Regional Plan Association of New York estimates that, every weekday, 32 million one-way trips that cover 190 million miles are made in this area, and over three million commuters enter the nine square mile section of New York south of 61st Street. It seems clear that the economic, social, and cultural opportunities of urban living are being sought by more and more people. An important advantage is that one is more likely to be able to change jobs without having to move.

But, says transportation expert Wilfred Owen, metropolitan cities have now grown to the point where they threaten to strangle the transportation that made them possible. A new "law" of transportation says: The longer the distance, the

The
Megalopolis
of
"Bosnywash"

shorter the time needed to cover it. And indeed, it does often take longer to drive from the heart of Manhattan to La Guardia Airport—a distance of about seven miles—than it does to fly from the airport to Boston (220 miles) or even Detroit (650 miles). In the fifteen years from 1948 to 1963, average ground time between CBD (Central Business District) and airport in the fifteen largest cities increased 38 per cent, or 23 minutes. This more than negated reductions in flight time resulting from improved flight routings and faster aircraft.

Today's Staggering Problems— and Some Suggested Answers

Every city in the United States is faced with a transportation problem of staggering proportions, one which will undoubtedly get worse before it gets better. All over the world, in fact, population is growing at an explosive pace; this can only mean greater transportation needs.

Two other factors which serve to increase the amount of passenger and freight movement are the continually larger areas being served by central cities, and higher incomes (at least in the more highly developed nations). As people move up the economic ladder, increased expenditure for transportation always follows.

At the same time, passengers have shifted increasingly from rail to road, putting gigantic strains on already antiquated and overburdened street systems. About half of all CBD land is occupied by streets, sidewalks, and parking. In areas which depend heavily on cars for transportation, such as Los Angeles,

14

the figure rises to almost two-thirds—just for streets and parking!

There is also the matter of safety. Every year in the United States alone, 50,000 people are killed and two million more are injured in automobile accidents. This is far, far more than in all other modes of transport combined, even when the higher proportion of auto travel is considered. Clearly, something must be done about this.

We see then that the problems are varied. We already mentioned the plight of the traveler who must switch from one system to another. An additional, and major, problem is the pendulum swing of commuters during the peak morning and evening "rush" hours. The tempers, time, and energy lost, and the air pollution produced, are beyond belief. The "speed" of traffic during these periods frequently falls to a few miles an hour, and sometimes to zero.

Subways, of course, do not have this problem. But while they do a fantastic job of moving great numbers of people in reasonable time, they are often more fit for sardines than humans during rush hours. Yet in the off hours they attract relatively few customers. The second problem, therefore, is how to provide satisfactory capacity during rush hours without having a lot of equipment and men doing nothing for the rest of the day, and particularly at night.

A third problem is providing for weekend and holiday travel. There isn't one of us living in or near a metropolitan area who hasn't battled ten to fifteen miles of creeping cars—and, of course, lost.

But what is simply inconvenience for us is "death" to certain types of businesses, particularly manufacturing and shipping. With improved roads and highways outside the cities, it

15

has been possible for many of them to move away from the CBD, to spread out into the suburbs. But this is exactly where the poor and unskilled, who provide most of the labor market for these industries, cannot live. The poor depend upon mass transit. However, population density in the suburbs is too low to support rail systems. Buses help, but they are subject to traffic tieups no less than cars.

Thus, the poor are moving into the city centers in great numbers, while their employers—the larger manufacturers particularly—are moving out. On the other hand, the skilled and white-collar workers are moving farther and farther out, leading often to two-hour commuting trips each way.

So the various problems we have mentioned boil down to this: How to provide safe, fast, convenient, comfortable transportation for both urban and suburban dwellers.

One of the answers has been the 41,000-mile Interstate Highway System, the most enormous public works project the world has ever seen, surpassing by far the Pyramids and the Great Wall of China. When completed sometime around 1972, the total cost is likely to exceed $60 billion.

Although these roads have certainly made travel a pleasure in many ways and in many areas, not everyone agrees that they are the answer. It is pointed out, for example, that they encourage auto travel, and thereby serve to funnel even more traffic into the already overburdened cities. It has been estimated that if all New York commuters were to arrive by car, every bit of land in the CBD would be required for parking— with some cars left over. And, as we shall see later, in addition to being expensive, these roads eat up land at a prodigious rate.

Nor does traffic always move smoothly. Not too long ago, a

16

New York reporter visited Los Angeles. After a ride along some of that city's fabulous freeways, he wrote back home: "I have seen the future, and it doesn't work."

The importance of the transportation problem is reflected in the recent creation of a new cabinet-level office in our government. For the first time in the history of the United States, there is a Department of Transportation, providing hope that a national transportation program and system can be devised which will solve some of the major problems.

The Department of Transportation Act was passed on October 15, 1966. It is worth reprinting here the first paragraph of the Act:

"The Congress hereby declares that the general welfare, the economic growth and stability of the Nation and its security require the development of national transportation policies and programs conducive to the provision of fast, safe, efficient, and convenient transportation at the lowest cost consistent therewith and with other national objectives, including the efficient utilization and conservation of the Nation's resources."

An important aspect of the new Secretary's job is that he is concerned with transportation as a whole. Thus, he won't be concerned with protecting the interests of the highway system, which has been under the mantle of the Bureau of Public Roads (and other bureaus), or of the airways, which have been the responsibility of the Federal Aviation Agency (and other agencies). Indeed, one of the major jobs of the new Secretary will be the pulling together of 100,000 people in more than thirty different agencies that now deal with air, rail, water, and highway transportation.

Another "tool" is the fact that this is a high-level office, with authority as well as responsibility. Through the consolidation of many scattered offices, and the creation of new ones, the Department should be able to cope with many problems which were well beyond the scope of any earlier agencies, and to cope as well with the many rivalries which were and still are inevitable.

Finally, there is science and technology—*research*. This may turn out to be the Secretary's most powerful tool. One of the advantages of a large agency is the availability of funds with which to encourage and support large-scale research which may come up with some answers to a many-sided problem.

For example, the fantastic spread of the auto has dampened the public's earlier enthusiasm for rail transportation. Many commuter railroads are either bankrupt or on the way. Many have had to be taken over by state agencies. Service is slow, inconvenient, and getting worse.

The problem compounds itself. No system can afford to operate only during peak hours. So men are laid off and equipment is retired. This impairs service even more, and more riders are lost. One suburban line in New Jersey, once a thriving activity, now runs only three trains a day. A recent traffic study shows that 94 per cent of those who both live and work in the suburbs use autos for their commuting.

The issue in recent years has been trains *vs.* cars. Stated this way, there is no right answer. Rather, the question should be how best to utilize both systems, for both are needed. Here is where technology can come to the rescue.

Systems are being looked at which may combine the best features of the two. The result might be an automatic expressway such as Andrew Mann used in our Prologue, or perhaps trains carrying cars "piggy-back." Both approaches are currently being considered and some test equipment has already been built.

Systems like these, and many others both near and far-out, shall be our major concern in the following chapters.

2

Rail Rapid
Transit

THE FIRST transit system in the United States was a "public stage." For a fee, it shuttled New Yorkers between Bowling Green at the lower tip of Manhattan, and Bleeker Street (which was all of one and three-quarter miles to the north).

The stages—horse-drawn carriages—made their first runs in 1830 and were private enterprises. They catered to a slowly growing middle-class rather than to the poor, who could not afford such luxuries, or to the rich, who had their own horses and buggies.

A few years later, the first railroad lines began taking people out into the country. In the case of New York, this meant going all the way up to what is now mid-Manhattan for picnics and outings.

The next major development in transit travel came in the

1890's. Rising wages for skilled workers increased demand for transit, while at the same time low wages for laborers made transit facilities cheap to build. Suddenly, every American city, and many towns, sprouted shining new lines of trolley track. Trolleys, or streetcars, were more convenient for local travel than railroads, since they traveled on the local streets and could stop at every corner if necessary. Furthermore, they provided a far smoother ride than stages, which moved upon the lumpy, bumpy cobblestones or plain dirt that were the common surfaces then. The rails also made life much easier for the horses still pulling the stages.

Electrification of the trolley systems made them cleaner and more exciting. In the early 1900's, New York City alone had 683 miles of trolley track within the city limits. It was even possible to ride all the way up to Boston on trolley tracks, paying 48 five-cent fares along the way. The idea of the modern megalopolis may sound like a new one, but this aspect of the several-hundred-mile city was evident more than half a century ago.

But trolleys, having neither the speed advantage conferred by the railroad's exclusive right-of-way, nor the flexibility of the bus, lost out to both. Because no exclusive rights-of-way were involved, the disappearance of trolley lines caused no major dislocations. The tracks, most of which had been laid in existing streets, were simply taken out or covered over.

The railroads, on the other hand, continued to grow. Indeed, the nineteenth and early twentieth centuries saw the railroads grow from humble beginnings to arrogant giants. So powerful, so confident were the managements of their monopoly position in the field of transportation that they ignored the threat of those two youngsters, the automobile and, not

21

much later, the aircraft. There was little concern or planning for the future.

It turns out that the rails in railroading, once the basis for its strength, are now its curse. For the truth is that, in many areas, the rails simply do not run to the right places any more. They are not where the "action" is.

Central cities with a population of a million or more—where the railroad is feasible (suitable for commuting, for example)—increased an average of only 2.8 per cent in the years from 1950 to 1960. In the same period, the suburbs jumped by 55.6 per cent. Once, cities and towns had to be centered on railroad stations and depots; with the development of motor vehicle and air transportation, this is no longer necessary.

But rights-of-way, once obtained, and rails, once laid, are not easily transferred. The investment in existing rights-of-way and rail lines is gigantic.

It is tempting to say, "If the railroads are not economically sound, if people prefer cars, then let the railroads go the way of the horse and buggy and the streetcar. Let the laws of supply and demand make the decision."

This would be shortsighted, and even unfair. What happens then to the young, the old, the infirm, or even those who, for various reasons, prefer not to own cars? Let us remember, too, the problem of congestion that we have already mentioned. And in many areas, the airlanes are almost as clogged as the highway lanes below them. It is not unusual for an aircraft to have to circle an overloaded airport for half an hour, waiting for room to land.

A single rail line can carry far more passengers than a lane of highway—depending on circumstances, from five to twenty times as many. Since population is increasing in urban areas, it may be that rail lines that are not profitable now may again become so later on, especially with the help of some developments we shall discuss as we go along.

New York State Buys a Railroad

Once lost, a railroad line is not easily replaced, and it could be a serious loss. A good example is the Long Island Rail Road in New York. It is a commuter line and the nation's busiest railroad. It carried almost 74 million passengers in 1966. Yet it has been losing money for years, so much in fact that its former "parent," the Penn Central Railroad, had no interest in putting more money into it. This was becoming necessary just to prevent further deterioration of equipment and service.

The Long Island Rail Road was bought by New York State. The cost for the entire system, with its 320 miles of right-of-way, its equipment, management, and skilled work force, was $65 million. Dr. William C. Ronan, chairman of the newly created New York Metropolitan Transportation Authority, points out:

> "This sum wouldn't have built two miles of the Cross-Bronx Expressway. We think we got a pretty good deal. . . . The cost of alternate highways—26 lanes of expressways plus new tunnels—would be over a billion and a half dollars, and there would be no place to park the cars. When our modernization program is in full swing, this investment will pay off many times over in economic growth and development of New York City and all of Long Island."

23

The modernization program referred to by Dr. Ronan is a $200-million-plus investment by the state, and includes new 100-mile per hour commuter cars which are carpeted, walnut paneled, and fully air-conditioned. Experiments are in progress on cars which can use third-rail electric power when available, or their own turbine engines in non-electrified areas farther out. Both types provide higher acceleration capability than the currently used diesels. The acceleration factor is an important one, for much time is lost in getting the heavy trains back up to speed after each stop.

When the program is in full swing, some time in the early 1970's, commuting time between Manhattan and Long Island cities will be cut by as much as 50 per cent.

Even more hopeful is the fact that a railroad commuter train may soon ride over city subway tracks. After all, both tracks measure 4 feet 8½ inches from rail to rail. This would eliminate a bothersome change for many riders at Penn Station, which is currently the only Long Island Rail Road stop in Manhattan.

The objective of the Metropolitan Transportation Authority is to provide better service by "meshing" all the services—subway, bus, commuter train, cars, and perhaps even aircraft. A conceptual drawing of what a multi-mode terminal would look like is shown.

When asked about such far-out ideas as the pneumatic tube or the air-cushion vehicle, Dr. Ronan replied, "We've had a good many ideas presented to us, and have gone out to look for new ideas. But for our purposes of moving great masses of people in the metropolitan region, we have not found anything in all these ideas yet that compares with two rails and steel wheels running on them."

A Multi-Mode Terminal

Considering the fact that the cities of the future will be getting larger, this is something to keep in mind. But, as we might expect in a complicated matter like this, not everyone agrees with him. A number of proposals have been made, and at least one system installed, in which rubber tires are used.

The Montreal Metro

Let us, for example, take a ride on the Montreal Metro. Eight big tires on each car ride on pre-cast concrete runways, providing a smooth, silent ride far different from the swaying

25

The Montreal Metro

clackety-clack of the usual subway. The system is cleaner, too, for the rubber tires do not generate the dust that steel wheels on steel rails do. A special, nightly vacuum-train picks up whatever dust does arise.

The trains are guided by small, horizontal, rubber wheels which press against vertical rails, so that the likelihood of the cars riding off the tracks is reduced almost to zero. As a super-safety measure, the designers added a set of steel wheels which ride above steel rails and only contact them if tires should go flat. The steel wheels are also used for switching purposes, which would be a problem with rubber tires.

When the motorman pushes the lever to Full Forward, a computer takes over for smooth acceleration. This is important because of the high acceleration rate of the train, which has

26

been aided by a clever arrangement. By building each station at the top of a slight grade, the train is helped by gravity to slow down when it arrives at a station, and to accelerate as it departs. Thanks to rapid starts and stops, plus automatic controls throughout the system, trains can operate during rush hours with a ninety-second headway—one train every minute-and-a-half.

This is enough to carry 60,000 passengers an hour on one line. Automobile expressways can barely manage 1,500 or 2,000 cars per lane per hour. Figuring two passengers in a car—the true average is about 1.5—this adds up to only 4,000 passengers per lane per hour, or only one-twentieth the capacity of the rail line.

The Montrealers have paid a little extra for architectural elegance and decoration, and are delighted with "the most beautiful subway in the world." A different architect has designed each station. The Berri-de Montigny station, where the Metro's two lines cross, is like a Parisian arcade. It is a block-long mezzanine of shops, bookstores, and flower stalls in a setting of handsome granite floors, pastel tile walls, and garden benches. In other words, subways don't have to be dirty and ugly.

Has the Metro been a commercial success? Indeed, it has. Revenues are 30 per cent above even the most optimistic estimates.

Experiments in Automation

But how about medium-density areas, where it is not economical to build, maintain, and run a complex, large-scale rail transit system? As explained earlier, where traffic is not heavy, the cost of manning and running the normal train or subway becomes prohibitive. Are such areas to be denied the acknowledged advantages of a rail system? Not if Westinghouse Electric has its way.

With help from government and industry, Westinghouse has developed a rapid transit system, the *Transit Expressway,* which promises to bridge the gap. Among the advantages claimed for the system are:

Economy—smaller, lighter cars are used, hence both structures and cars are cheaper to build and maintain.

Flexibility—since the cars are self-propelled, from one to ten vehicles can be used in each "train." A two-minute headway is proposed *around the clock,* with cars moving at up to 50 mph.

But the real shock is what makes all this possible: *entirely automatic operation.* An automatic train control system has been developed which does all the "driving."

Actually, of course, this should no longer surprise us. After all, self-service elevators have been around for quite a while.

Westinghouse's Transit Expressway

Control Center for Transit Expressway

The important point here is that labor costs constitute a major part of the expenses in conducting transportation.

As shown in the photo, a demonstration Transit Expressway has actually been built and tested. A monitor system on each vehicle continually checks the operation of operating equipment and indicates to the Central Control point any malfunction on the car. It even specifies the degree of the problem so that appropriate action can be taken. In addition, a two-way communication channel is provided between the vehicles and Central Control. In this way, announcements can be made to the passengers and, in case an emergency does arise, passengers can communicate with Central Control.

A transit system based on the Transit Expressway principle is being built at the Tampa Airport to shuttle passengers between terminal and aircraft, a distance of about 1,000 feet. And a full-scale system is being considered for use in and around the Pittsburgh area.

29

Is automatic operation of a rail system practical on a large scale? We are going to find out shortly. One of the most exciting developments in railway technology is under construction now.

When completed in the early 1970's, the $1.2 billion, 75-mile San Francisco transit system will be the first to be fully computerized and automated. Even fare collection will be automated. This will also be the first completely new rapid transit system to be built in the U.S. in sixty years. A prototype of one of the new cars is shown.

As in the Montreal Metro, thanks to automatic controls the trains will also be capable of 90-second headways. However, maximum speed will be about 80 miles per hour (mph), necessary because of the longer distances involved, as opposed to 60 for the Metro. No human brain could possibly react fast

The Bay Area Rapid Transit System

enough to handle reliably a series of trains moving that fast and that close together. The control system will dispatch the trains, keep them on schedule, and maintain the proper interval between them.

Indeed, the computer will continually monitor and, when necessary, adjust train schedules and performance. This should go far to eliminate the gaps in service that are one of the most irritating factors in using public transport. Because of the greater density of expected traffic, it will be economically feasible for an attendant to ride each train.

As with the Westinghouse system, two-way voice communication is provided. In case of emergency, the attendant will be able to operate the train at slow speed after obtaining permission from the central office.

The system called Bay Area Rapid Transit, or BART, is expected to spur the growth of San Francisco, Oakland, and Berkeley as a three-city core area. At the same time, this core area will be linked to various surrounding suburban communities, providing a framework for an organized pattern of future growth outward from these established areas.

A different kind of plan, for the Washington, D.C., metropolis of the future, proposes a stellar arrangement, with the CBD at the center and each ray of the star coordinated with a rapid transit line.

Similarly, a 5.5 mile "Linear City" has been proposed for Brooklyn, N.Y., in which all the elements of a city—residence, work, educational facilities, and recreation—would be located along and carefully interlocked with a combined rapid transit and highway system. It would be almost like a large corporation operating on a number of floors of a skyscraper.

Personnel interaction between the floors depends upon speedy elevator service. Activities along the linear city would similarly depend upon speedy, reliable service which, thanks to a high density population, could be provided. Land normally lost to a highway or ground-level tracks would then be used in an attractive, convenient arrangement. Thus, a worker or student could go down to the basement of his apartment house and take a shuttle to work or school.

In another approach to mating rapid transit and housing, a Stockholm, Sweden, suburb uses the following planning rule: Suburban apartments should be within about ¼-mile, and single-family houses within ½-mile, of a rapid transit station.

In most cases, however, rail lines are above ground, which brings up the problem of the usually ugly appearance of tracks and railroad rights-of-way. BART, most of whose trackage is on or above ground, also faces this problem. As a result, and because of the significance of the program, America's first Urban Beautification Demonstration grant has gone to BART.

Worth almost half a million dollars, the grant will be used on a 2.7 mile stretch of the system to demonstrate how the right-of-way under an aerial structure can be treated so that it will be attractive and hence more acceptable to the communities through which it passes. Any of you who have experienced the dark dreariness under the normal elevated structure will appreciate the value of this approach. The objective is to create a sort of "linear park" along and under the tracks which is both attractive and useful.

An additional benefit will be a more pleasant ride for the passengers. Recent work in materials technology promises high-strength materials which will permit supporting structures to be even slimmer and more attractive in the future.

Monorails

When speaking of modern rail technology, one almost always thinks of the monorail: sleek trains gracefully suspended from a single track. Yet, contrary to the usual notion, the first of them was built more than a century ago. Still, they somehow always seem to be just around the corner. While they are often seen at world's fairs (e.g., at both the Seattle and New York World's Fairs) and on test tracks, they have found little commercial use.

One notable exception is the monorail at Wuppertal, Germany, which carried more than a billion passengers between 1901 and 1966. In 1964, Tokyo built one linking its airport with the center of the city, a distance of 8.2 miles. This was actually a duo-rail, about which we will read more shortly.

One of the advantages cited for use of the monorail is the fact that only a single rail need be put up for each line. With improved rail construction techniques, this advantage has faded somewhat. Also, monorail cars tend to sway and often require special horizontal wheels and tracks, thus negating the supposed simplicity of the system.

Perhaps some sort of compromise has been reached with General Electric's proposal for an *Aerial Transport System*. Based on a French system, the SAFEGE, it seems at first glance to be a monorail system; but it isn't, at least not in the normal sense of the word. The system uses rubber wheels running on a pair of enclosed overhead tracks, and therefore offers quiet, smooth, and reliable operation under all weather conditions.

33

General Electric's Aerial Transport System

Clearly, it offers great advantages in low or medium density, cold-weather areas. Speeds of 100 mph are said to be quite feasible, even in ice and sleet which normally make both air and surface travel slow and even hazardous. Again, completely automatic operation can make this a highly reliable and economical system. The latter factor becomes particularly marked when the Aerial Transport System is compared to subways, which are very expensive to build.

The illustration shows its possible usage as a direct connection between an airport (such as Dulles International, located about 25 miles from downtown Washington, D.C.) and the center of town.

The *single-track* arrangement shown might even be feasible

34

right in or around the heart of a city, as a loop. That is, all trains would run in the same direction around a more or less circular track. The single track (or track pair) would take up less room than the normal two-way arrangement. Since CBD's are usually small, the passenger would not lose much time by having to travel, for example, three-quarters of the way around the loop to get to his destination.

One big advantage of any monorail type system is the small amount of surface area it requires. It is a natural for operation in built-up, though not heavily congested, areas. Supporting columns can be set in the center parkway of a street, if available, or just back from the edge of the sidewalk. In the event of a narrow sidewalk, the trainway can be cantilevered out over the street as shown. In each of these arrangements there is no restriction of full use of the street.

Naturally, such suspension-type systems need not be confined to elevated travel. Indeed, such use only makes sense in medium-density districts. In highly congested areas, they can be routed underground like any subway. And in suburban areas or between cities, the cars can travel at surface level. Obviously, however, when run in these modes, suspension systems lose some of the advantage they had over conventional rail systems.

Clearly, each application must be evaluated on the basis of its own problems, traffic requirements, and whether it is exclusively city or suburban, or a combination of both.

In general, rapid transit proposals and projects are concentrated in large, established regional centers with present or future urban populations of more than 1.5 million people. It is well known even now that the larger the city, the higher the

35

Coordinated Use of Land for Rapid Transit and Autos

proportion of transit travel into and out of the downtown area.

In a number of cities, such as New York, Chicago, Newark, Philadelphia, Richmond, Boston, Atlanta, and Cleveland, from one-half to three-quarters of all persons entering the CBD do so by some form of rail transportation. A recent study indicated that peak-hour traffic congestion in a city can be cut to a tolerable level by reducing the number of autos entering the CBD by one-fourth. In one well-coordinated arrangement in Chicago, rapid transit carries 50 per cent more people than the four-lane expressway alongside it, yet adds only 10 per cent to the construction cost. The illustration shows how this might work in some city of the future.

One clever comment on the auto/rail question was made by Dr. R. E. Packer, engineer and author. He said, "Every driver wants rapid transit—because he hopes it will remove the driver in front of him."

The truth of the matter is that travel by public transportation is strongly conditioned by a number of factors which are *not* directly related to the quality of available service. Examples are level of family income, automobile ownership, and density of urban development. It has even been pointed out that the American West was won by men on horseback, and that many men still have a similar feeling for their cars.

The question is, can these men be pried from their saddles? We have seen that innovations in rail systems offer some hope that they can. In later chapters, we will discuss other approaches to the commuter problem and to travel *within* the city as well. In the meantime, let us see what rail-type transportation offers to the medium- and long-distance traveler of the future.

High Speed Ground Transportation

A RELATIVELY short time ago, man learned to harness the energy of steam, thus inaugurating a fantastic century and a half of progress in transportation. What engine-driven transportation immediately provided was a combination of comfort and speed.

Plush accommodations were nothing new. Marine navigation had been supplying that (for special people of course) for centuries—although with some accompanying annoyances such as occasional dampness and seasickness. The coach-and-six, too, was often a small palace on wheels. Royal coaches often had gilded decorations and beautifully carved woods, gorgeous velvet linings, built-in lanterns, and even chamber pots. But the iron-bound wooden wheels bouncing along on bad roads generally required the traveler to have insides of iron, especially if any speed at all was required. Springs helped, but not much.

The development of the train was a major improvement, for the combination of comfort and speed was something quite new in the history of transportation. Although the railroad started out with rather slow speeds and spartan conditions, both improved rapidly. Prophets who forecast suffocation for anyone traveling faster than 30 mph were shortly shown to be wrong. The ante was raised to 60 mph. Again, this imaginary speed barrier was breached in short order.

The first steam-powered train built expressly for rails ran in England in 1804. The very first trip carried ten tons of iron, five wagons, and seventy men. It took four hours to cover 9½ miles, for a sparkling average of just over two miles an hour.

But it was a start, and by 1849 European express trains could hit 75 mph, a respectable speed even now. In 1893, the American locomotive 999 set a world's record: 100 mph. While this was exciting, what was going on in the American West was even more so. What red-blooded American youngster has not thrilled to the exploits of the brave railroaders? Who can doubt that it was the railroad which finally pried open the American West? Hard though it may be to believe, it was not until a century ago that the eastern and western coasts of the United States were directly linked by rail. It was on May 10, 1869, that the final, ceremonial golden spike was driven.

For a long time, the railroad was the ultimate in travel. And it grew quickly, not only in America, but also all over the world. England had 1,600 miles of rail by 1841, and 6,890 only ten years later. By the mid-1800's, some trains had become virtual hotels on wheels, with comfortable beds, chandeliers, thick carpets, velvet draperies, even libraries, and good food. (In America, at least, one had the choice of elk, antelope, buffalo, beefsteak, mutton, or grouse.)

But far more important was the question of trip time. The trip between the east and west coasts of the United States had once taken five to six months by wagon; it could be made in three months by fast clipper around Cape Horn. Suddenly, the journey could be made in five or six days! There was nothing to compare with it.

Now, a full century later, it still takes three days—an improvement of 100 per cent. Compared to the increased speeds of aircraft and even ships over their early days, this is hardly any improvement at all.

Problems of the Railroads

Of course, jet aircraft now make the trip in about five hours. Does this mean that, except for commuting purposes, the passenger train is doomed? For a number of years now, this has seemed to be the case. For the long-haul train it is almost certainly true, at least for the railroad train as we know it today. After a study of eleven western railroads, the Stanford Research Institute concluded that the long-haul, intercity train "seems destined to disappear from the American scene."

Oddly enough, many railroad companies are delighted with this conclusion. For example, it supports a request made to the Interstate Commerce Commission by the Western Pacific

Railroad to discontinue the operation of its California *Zephyr*. Thanks to outstanding scenery and service, the *Zephyr*, operating between Chicago and the San Francisco Bay area, is one of the most popular trains in the west. Yet it is losing $2,000 a day.

One of the problems is that the schedule, set to afford the best daytime viewing, is not convenient for local (non-tourist) patronage. A second is that the equipment, put into service in 1949, will soon need replacement. Finally, although the west has grown steadily and other forms of transportation have experienced increased passenger traffic, the Zephyr has only managed to hold its own—in spite of the fact that it is jammed to capacity during the summer months.

For all railroads, the story has been no better, and generally worse. Rising costs, dwindling traffic, and, as a result of competition from other forms of transportation, lowered fares, have put the squeeze on. Most make up their losses in passenger activities from freight income. In 1967, the nation's largest railroad, the Penn Central, earned about $73 million in its freight operations, but lost $58 million in its passenger operations.

Many railroads, therefore, are anxious to drop certain of their least profitable lines. They cannot do this arbitrarily, however. They must present their case to the Interstate Commerce Commission (the ICC), a federal regulating agency which balances the problems of the railroads against the needs of the areas served. (The ICC was established by Congress in 1887, as a reaction against railroad malpractices such as over-charging and other abuses of their power.) Yet, according to the Stanford study, "The field must be abandoned sooner or later to the swifter airplane, the cheaper and more

41

convenient bus, and the infinitely more flexible private automobile."

While it is unlikely that the railroad—at least in its present
state of development—can ever regain its previous eminence,
there are hopeful signs for the future. This is especially true
for the medium-distance trip of 100 to 400 miles, which is
today more often taken by car, bus, or aircraft.

The first two modes certainly don't help the highway situation. Even in the case of aircraft, highway travel is normally
involved, i.e., getting to and from the airport by car, bus, or
limousine. There are only a few cities in the entire world
where it is possible to get from city center to airport by rail.

Tokyo's monorail and the Brussels subway are two excep-
tions. When completed, the Cleveland link will be a third. And,
as part of a sweeping $2.9 billion blueprint for expanding
and consolidating New York City's mass-transit facilities, the
Long Island Rail Road may provide a fourth. A spur off the
main line would make possible direct, 20-minute service from
Manhattan to Kennedy International Airport. The trip is now
an uncertain 30-60 minute car or bus ride, or an expensive
10-14 minute helicopter ride.

When looked at from the overall point of view, the question
must not be, "How fast does the vehicle travel?" or even,
"How long does it take to fly from New York to Washington?"
Rather the question should be phrased, "How long does the
trip take from door to door?"

By car, the trip from New York to Washington, D.C., is
normally a hard five-hour drive. The plane trip is under an
hour, but connections and local travel generally bring the total
up to two and a half hours or so. Another problem with plane
travel lies in a certain amount of undependability. As we have

mentioned, traffic in the skies, particularly in the northeast, is not much better than on the ground.

Weather, too, can play havoc with plane schedules. It is not unusual to make the plane trip in lightning time and then circle the airport for half or three-quarters of an hour before being allowed to land. (This is similar to being stuck in a traffic jam on a highway leading into a city.)

The advantages offered by train travel are transportation from city center to city center, comfort, and good dependability. If the schedule says arrival at 3 P.M., you can be quite sure that that is the time you will get there, at least on the better railroads.

The problem with trains seems now to be speed, or lack of it. Let us return to the New York–Washington run. We figured the car trip for five hours, and the plane for two and a half. How about the train?

The afternoon *Congressional* leaves New York at 4:30 P.M., makes four intermediate stops—at Newark, Philadelphia, Wilmington, and Baltimore—and arrives at the nation's capitol at 8:05. This is just over three and a half hours. With additional connections at the ends of the trip, an average total might be four hours.

But these trains are limited to speeds of 80 mph. If train speeds could be raised to 100 mph, the train could arrive in Washington at 7:30; at 125 mph, it could arrive at 7:09; and at 150 mph, at 6:48. This last trip would take just over two hours; many commuters spend this much time getting to work every day.

The Super-Express

What are the prospects for such speeds? The Japanese are well on their way. Using standard, though improved, rail techniques, super-express trains speed between Tokyo and Osaka at up to 125 mph.

In addition, service is excellent. There are the *Hikari* (lightning) trains that run every hour in each direction and, with stops at Nagoya and Kyoto, make the 360 miles in three hours. Then there are also the *Kodama* (echo) trains on the half-hour which, with nine stops, make the run in three and a half hours.

These trains run on a completely new double track and are automated to a large degree. They carry only passengers, no freight. However, high-speed freight shipments have been suggested for the midnight to early morning hours, when no passenger trains are run.

So successful is the super-express that it has taken business away from the airlines, a most unusual turnabout. The area served, incidentally, is strikingly similar to our own Northeast Corridor. Between the two ends of the line there are two major metropolitan areas, which account for 40 per cent of the nation's population, but nearly 70 per cent of the industrial output.

It must be remembered, however, that the level of car ownership in Japan is much lower than in the United States. Hence, the question of whether a similar, or even more advanced, railroad system would do as well in the United States might have quite a different answer.

Would it, for example, serve the needs of an area like the

Japanese Super-Express Trains

Northeast Corridor with its 38 million people and the heaviest traffic in the nation? (Population planners tell us that the area will have 50 to 55 million people by 1980.) Can it become popular enough to relieve some of the pressure on both the highways and the airways? Would the comfort and luxury that train travel could provide make the difference?

These are important questions, which we may see answered in the next few years. In 1965, even before the creation of the Department of Transportation, Congress passed the High Speed Ground Transportation Act. Included in the program is a three-year experiment designed to improve rail travel in the Northeast Corridor. This project, undertaken jointly with the Penn Central Railroad, is the first government-sponsored research on behalf of the railroads.

"It could conceivably lead," says Penn Central Railroad Chairman Stuart Saunders, "to the same kind of spectacular breakthroughs in rail transportation technology that have resulted from government-sponsored research and development in aviation."

The program is divided into two parts. The first concerns improvements in existing rail technology, and the second will investigate the potential of unconventional ground transportation.

Improvements in Technology

An important aspect of the first category is the use of four highly instrumented *test cars*. The specially built cars are electrically driven, self-propelled, and capable of top speeds of 150 mph. A special 21-mile track has been prepared on the Penn Central line between Trenton and New Brunswick, New Jersey, since good track is imperative for a smooth and safe ride at these high speeds. Fourteen probes installed on the truck of one test car check track conditions.

Results show how the specially prepared rail bed is affected by trains traveling at various speeds and loads. The familiar clackety-clack is nowhere in evidence, for at high speeds the small spaces between the butting ends of conventional rails would be dangerous. All the rails in high-speed equipment must be of the new, welded variety.

Each of the four cars is instrumented to test a different set of conditions, such as rail alignment, smoothness of ride, lateral sway, vibration, and noise level. It is significant that the instrumentation, which includes closed-circuit television, gyros, accelerometers, and a multitude of electronic devices, has been supplied by Melpar, Inc., a company with wide experience in the aerospace field.

The testing of *new rail equipment* is an important part of the program. The cars are also being used as "test beds" for all kinds of equipment, such as wheels, trucks, motors, suspension systems, propulsion other than electric, new controls —indeed, almost anything that promises a significant improvement.

Fifty cars, which will incorporate the best results of the tests, have been ordered from the Budd Company. These will be used in the demonstration program which promises half-hourly service from New York to Philadelphia and hourly service to Washington—a 50 per cent increase in service. Although the test cars have already reached 156 mph, top speed of the new trains will he held initially to 110 mph.

When conditioning of the right-of-way for the high-speed trains is completed, the Penn Central will have installed 404 miles of continuous welded rail in strings 1,440 feet long, more than 180 miles of overhead electrical wire in a revamped suspension and take-off system, and more than 250,000 cross ties. This gives some idea of what is involved in merely modernizing a system.

A different aspect of the experiment consists of two *park-and-ride stations* which are to be constructed in New Jersey and Maryland, near expressways. These will test the potential of such facilities to lure the motorist away from crowded metropolitan highways. (Alternatives are to have the wife deliver and pick up her husband by car, or to have one or more bus routes terminate at the station.)

The northern part of the Corridor (New York to Boston)

An American Turbine-Powered Express

presents a somewhat different set of problems. Here there are
many more curves on the railroad line, and many parts are
not electrified. Two *turbine-powered trains* have been tested
for use on this line. Again, it is significant that the test trains,
although built by Pullman-Standard (a train manufacturer),
were developed by United Aircraft. The company is guarantee-
ing a top speed of 160 mph, although top speed will be held to
110-120 mph at first. The test train consists of a three-car unit,
with the fore and aft cars containing the gas turbines.

These engines are one of the most significant aspects of
the new trains. They are light in weight but very powerful,
having been developed originally for aircraft. Each power
dome car contains from two to four of these engines, depending on the train's makeup and schedule, but will also be

equipped to pick up power from a third rail so that it can operate in tunnels like those in Manhattan.

Other innovations are lightweight bodies and a new form of suspension described as *pendulous*. The system is intended to bank the train into the curves just as an aircraft does, rather than allowing the car bodies to try to lean outward as they normally do. This approach, along with a low center of gravity, is expected to enable the equipment to round the many curves on this run at speeds 30 to 40 per cent higher than trains can take today. Aircraft-type streamlining is another factor important at the high speeds expected.

In other words, the technology of steel wheels on steel tracks is being pushed hard, perhaps to its ultimate end. With increase of speed, the problem of driving and braking, depending as it does on the friction between smooth wheels and rails, meets definite limits (the question of just what these limits are has not yet been definitely decided). For example, high-speed racing cars sometimes use airfoils to force them *down* in order for the tires to maintain a good grip on the surface. This is necessary because, at high speeds, the vehicle itself begins to act like an airfoil.

At these speeds, even small surface irregularities on the tracks produce vertical motions which reduce the firmness of contact. While a number of researchers feel that, at 160 mph, we are nearing the safe speed limits of this class of vehicles, we shall see later that the feeling is not universal.

New and Unconventional Systems

All of this bring us to the next part of our discussion and the second part of the High Speed Ground Transportation study: namely, *unconventional systems*. One of the major areas of investigation is a possible substitute for the wheel. There are actually several aspects to the question, which normally resolve themselves into the areas of suspension, propulsion, and braking. The last two can be, and often are, considered together.

Methods of suspension for high speed vehicles fall into three general classes: mechanical contact, magnetic forces and fluid pressure.

The first, *mechanical contact*, refers to sliding or rolling members. Sliding surfaces are definitely out because of the great amount of frictional resistance and heat involved. By rolling members, we mean wheels, of course, but also rollers or any other similar kind of approach. The point is to keep an open mind and not eliminate an approach which might prove useful.

Nevertheless, as we have said, there is a general feeling that this general class of suspension may not be practical for high-speed travel. Professors W. W. Seifert and R. J. Hanson of the Massachusetts Institute of Technology point out that there is a tendency for various "dynamic instabilities" to occur as speed is increased. Thus, they maintain, in the speed range of 200 mph and up, conventional suspension technology is almost certain to be inadequate even when vehicles are operated over the smoothest guideways.

As with the mechanical contact class, there are also various approaches to *fluid suspension*. Among them are air cushions, air bearings, and aerodynamic lifting surfaces. In the last case, the vehicle is simply flying. This, in combination with a track, can cause trouble.

For example, a gust of wind might throw the vehicle against the track, or even into a nose dive. In aircraft there is room to overcome such activities. Not here. However, we shall see in a moment that this effect does become useful when used in conjunction with the air cushion mode. Air bearings and air pads have not found application because of the high pressures required and other difficult technical problems.

On the other hand, there is a great deal of activity in the air cushion field. A half-scale model of a tracked *Air-Cushion Vehicle* (*ACV*) has already been built and is being tested in France. The experimental model carries five passengers and a driver at a speed of about 125 mph. The Bertin *Aerotrain* looks like a sleek one-car commuter special except for the propulsion —a single aero engine and propeller. With the use of a turbo jet engine to test high speed "flight," the car has reached a speed of 215 mph.

The next model was designed to carry 80 passengers at a cruising speed of 155 mph. Top speed will be 186 mph without augmented power. Also on the drawing board is a design that will provide top speeds of up to 250 mph.

As can be seen in drawing *a*) on page 54, the Aerotrain rides on a cushion of air produced by outlets at the bottom of the vehicle. Thus, there is no friction problem. It can also be seen that air pressure keeps the car lined up on the track; minor irregularities in the track produce no instabilities in the motion of the craft. The straightness of the vertical stem will be checked by laser instruments about once a year.

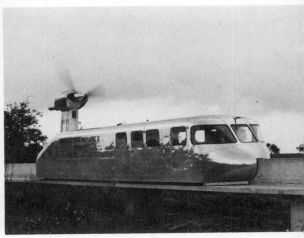

Bertin's Aerotrain

It is interesting to note that the pressure required is quite low. Only about .35 pounds per square inch (above atmospheric) is needed on the smaller model, and something over half a pound on the newer models. An automobile tire requires roughly 20 pounds per square inch. The reason that such low pressures can be used in the ACV is that the air is spread out over a large surface, and is more or less contained by flexible "skirts" before it leaks out into the atmosphere.

At high speeds, three-fourths of the installed lifting power can be diverted to propulsion because of a "ram effect." Some of the air in front of the vehicle is literally shoved into the space under the car, thus automatically providing lift.

Braking is accomplished in one or more of three different ways. First, the pitch of the propeller is reversed, as is done on some aircraft today after landing. Second, a pair of "pads" grabs the vertical rail, which shows surprisingly little wear

52

after some 10,000 miles of trial runs along the 4.2 mile track. In case of trouble, the engine is simply cut off. Without the supporting air, the Aerotrain skids along the guideways on a series of wooden runners, each about a foot long. Even so, at 155 mph it takes 20 seconds and 800 yards for the train to come to a full stop.

The English and Americans, too, are hard at work on ACV systems. (See page 54.) The English entry is the HDL (Hovercraft Development, Ltd.) *Hovercar,* or *Hovertrain,* shown in *b.* This system uses a form of vertical guidance slightly different from the Aerotrain, although the principle is the same. The General Motors *Hovair,* shown schematically in *c,* combines the action of guidance and suspension, as shown. For switching purposes, the track is simply flattened out. This can be done with the Aerotrain too, although at present the craft is turned around on a large turntable at the end of each run. Both the English and American entries are in the model-testing stage.

Because of the low requirements for smoothness and alignment of the guideway surface (clearly the word "rail" is no longer applicable), and the fact that the load is not concentrated in very small areas as they are on wheels, the construction costs for air cushion guideways can be very much lower than for any other form of ground transportation discussed so far.

There is an additional advantage to ACV's. Thanks to the spreading out of the air cushion, the vehicle is supported across the entire bottom surface rather than just at two ends, as in a normal train or bus. Hence the construction need not be as rigid, leading to lighter vehicles.

*   *   *

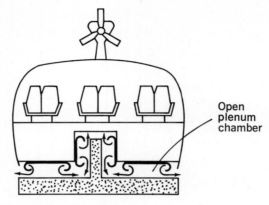

Open plenum chamber

AERO TRAIN (FRANCE)

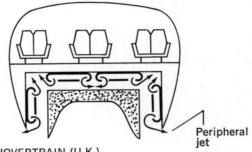

Peripheral jet

HOVERTRAIN (U.K.)

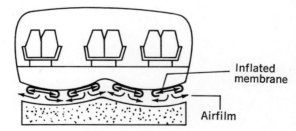

Inflated membrane

Airfilm

GM HOVAIR (U.S.)

Three Air-Cushion Vehicles:
a) the Aerotrain, b) the Hovertrain, and c) the Hovair

We turn now to *magnetic suspension systems,* those in which the means of supporting the craft above the guideway is magnetic. This might be compared to the repulsion experienced when you try to bring together two bar magnets with north poles facing.

Magnetic suspension systems are less well along than the air cushion types, mainly because very powerful fields are necessary to provide the required lifting forces. Developments in the science of low temperatures, however, have suggested a possible approach.

Under normal conditions, very high electric currents, needed to energize the powerful electromagnets, create high temperatures. Thus, much of the input power is lost in the form of heat. Conversely, at very low tempertures (and I do mean *low* —on the order of –450°F), metals become superconductive. That is, they offer no resistance at all to an electric current, and so there are no losses. At these "cryogenic" temperatures a current, once induced, can circulate for years with virtually no power loss.

Drs. G. T. Danby and J. R. Powell, scientists at Brookhaven National Laboratory, declare it is now possible to build inexpensive, magnetically-suspended trains that, with a relatively small power system, can lift a 100-foot, 100-passenger train. A proposed 300-mph train is shown in the drawing on the next page.

The pontoon-like housings contain superconducting coils that keep the train skimming a foot above the guideway, while a propeller at the rear drives the train. The coils would be made of niobium-titanium wire that is cooled close to absolute zero (—459°F) by a pipe containing a flow of liquid helium. At such low temperatures a large flow of current, in

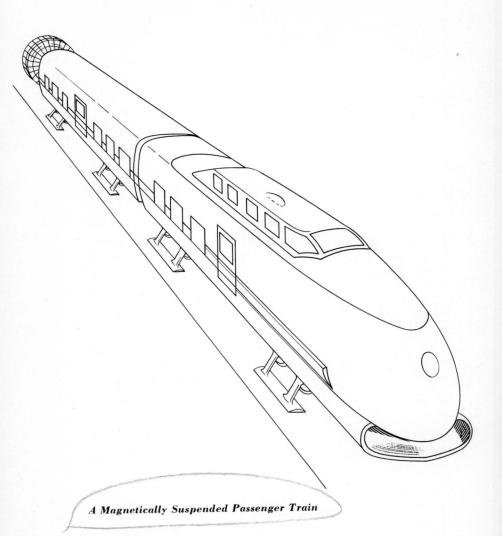

A Magnetically Suspended Passenger Train

this case 300,000 amps, can be fed through the coils without burning up the wire.

The track consists of electrical loops embedded in concrete which are activated only when the train passes over them. The loops are made in such a way that the train is kept centered over the guideway. So far this approach—that is, magnetic suspension—is still strictly conceptual.

Propulsion methods are not being ignored in these studies. We have already seen that both propellers and rockets are being considered for thrust. Such forms are necessary since there is no mechanical contact, namely wheels, between train and guideway. There are problems with these approaches, however. Among them are noise, heat blast, vibration, and air pollution (especially in tunnels). In addition, rocket fuel is expensive, and in jets there are hot, moving parts which are always subject to excessive wear and maintenance.

An interesting approach has been suggested. Let us recall that an electric motor generally has a central part, the rotor, which spins inside an outer case, the stator. Researchers are looking into the possibilities of using the so-called *"linear motor,"* in which one-half of an electric motor is in effect unwound and laid out flat along the guideway while the other half is in the vehicle. When electricity is passed through the windings of the system, the vehicle is "pulled" along the track in very much the same way that a normal rotor is moved around its axis, i.e., by electromagnetic forces.

Linear motors deserve consideration for a number of reasons. These include the lack of moving parts, less weight in the vehicle (thus saving both weight and space), and the fact that nothing is being burned.

The six-foot HDL Hovertrain model mentioned on page 53 is driven by just such a motor. The company is planning to construct a test track and a full-scale, 200-mph vehicle in the future. The AiResearch Corporation and other companies in the United States are also working on the linear motor for the Department of Transportation, and General Motors is considering this approach for its Hovair.

Another use for linear motors might be auxiliary devices for acceleration and deceleration in and near stations, for this is when the greatest power is needed. Once the train gets up to speed, much less power is needed to keep it going.

So far, we have been more or less loafing along at a few hundred miles per hour. In the next chapter, we begin to speed things up a bit.

4

Tunnels
and Tubes

On December 26, 1947, two friends and I were standing in Grand Central Station, waiting for the train to pull in that would take us north to Saranac Lake for a vacation. Since that was twenty years ago, I don't remember all the details, but a number of things are etched clearly in my mind. I know we waited several hours before the train even came into the station, and several more before it pulled out. We arrived at our destination twelve hours late.

The problem? A raging snowstorm was in the process of dumping several feet of snow all along the Northeast. Aircraft and most cars, buses, and trucks gave up quickly. The trains apparently got through, but not without a mighty struggle. The subways ran—and pretty much on time. I can vouch for this because we got to the station by subway.

The moral is clear. The only way to prevent a recurrence of

collapses of our transportation system is to *put transportation underground, or in some kind of enclosed guideway.* Nor is snow the only weather problem. Fog, rainstorms, hail, sleet, and even tornados and hurricanes all cause problems at one time or another in all parts of the United States.

But there is more reason even than this. We have seen that ground speeds of 100 mph or more call for exclusive rights-of-way, for example, rails. As the speeds of ground systems continue to increase, safety as well as all-weather considerations will make such a move absolutely necessary. For example, a car traveling at 100 mph or more is normally a sure candidate for trouble.

It is worth mentioning that rail systems have proved to be about the safest way to travel. During the period from 1940 to 1960, rail lines averaged only 1.22 passenger deaths per billion passenger miles traveled; air fatalities averaged 14.01; and highway fatalities averaged 31.3, or more than 25 times higher than the rail figure.

Nevertheless, speeds of several hundred miles an hour are unthinkable unless the trains are also protected from snow and ice and from objects falling into or crossing their path.

Almost any of the systems described in the last chapter could be used in a tube or tunnel. In a somewhat more futuristic vein, students at Tufts University proposed a 350 mph tube system a few years ago. A bullet-shaped, 75-passenger vehicle rests in its tube on retractable wheels. Driven by turbo-prop engines mounted front and rear, the vehicle begins to move. As it approaches 150 mph, the wheels retract and the vehicle is "flying," though protected from collision with the tube walls by a cushion of high-pressure air. Time from Boston to Washington: one and a half hours!

Because the engine exhaust fills the tube with hot, poisonous fumes, air conditioners have to be placed about every four miles along the route, and the vehicle must carry its own air supply. Stations are designed as giant turntables which move in a half-circle, thus sealing off the tubes before passengers can move in or out of the vehicles. A model was built by the students to test the feasibility of the system.

However, no matter how streamlined a vehicle may be, it still acts like a piston in a tube. In this case, the piston must be a very leaky one, or pressure buildup would finally prevent the craft from moving at all. At high speeds, a great deal of air per unit-time must move from front to rear of the vehicle through the space that separates it from the tube. This leads to problems with air resistance and heat buildup.

Propulsion and Suspension

An interesting proposal, made by Dr. J. V. Foa of the Rensselaer Polytechnic Institute, is to *use* this air in the propulsion scheme. In essence, thrust is generated by continuously transferring the air immediately in front of the vehicle to its rear. This is very similar to what happens in a jet engine, and indeed the vehicle itself can be regarded as the central body of a jet engine, the outer shroud or case of which is represented by the wall of the tube.

As the air is drawn into the "engine," it is heated; it then expands and escapes out the rear. This is the action. The vehicle is driven forward by the inevitable reaction. (Newton's third law of motion: Every action has an equal and opposite reaction.)

At very high speeds, the air is *forced* into the "engine," but the principle remains the same. The tube-vehicle system may thus be viewed as operating like a jet engine with no or very little drag. Although officially known as Project Tubeflight, the system has been nicknamed the *Air Gulper*.

Current technology calls for powering the craft with a conventional gas turbine engine. But this leaves us with the problem of noxious fumes, which are corrosive as well as dangerous in closed spaces. Furthermore, the craft must carry its own fuel supply, as well as air, which whittles down the potential payload.

It would be desirable to power the vehicle electrically—from the outside. However, this would be particularly difficult in the present case, since Dr. Foa would like to use a large-clearance fluid suspension system (at least several inches between craft and tube wall). An important advantage of the large clearance, says Dr. Foa, is the freedom of the vehicle to tilt itself to the correct angle of bank in every turn, regardless of the speed at which the turn is negotiated.

This is the same in principle as the pendulous suspension system used in the United Aircraft TurboTrain and adds greatly to the comfort and safety of the passengers. It also contributes to the economy of the guideway, since it permits greater curvatures in turns and makes it easier to avoid difficult or expensive terrain.

However, the large clearance makes use of the linear electric motor—the most obvious candidate—difficult, for the larger the gap between stator and "rotor," the lower the efficiency of the system. Suspended wires and third rails do not lend themselves to use at really high speeds.

An interesting possibility is to use high frequency, or microwave, energy. Because of its high frequency, such energy travels more efficiently in tubes (commonly called *waveguides*) than in wires. By choosing the proper frequency, it is possible to use the system's tube itself as the waveguide! Hence, energy can be beamed to the vehicle for propulsion and perhaps suspension and communication as well.

The principle has been demonstrated many times. For example, a five-pound helicopter model has been kept aloft by microwave energy transmitted from the ground. Also, since the energy will essentially "fill" the tube, the effect of any rolling motions of the vehicle during banking turns will not interfere with the power supply.

New Propulsion Ideas

Still other unusual modes of propulsion are being considered. One is an application of a relatively new field with the jawbreaking name, *magnetogasdynamics*. Here the interaction of charged gases and magnetic fields can be used to provide propulsion. The idea is still in the conceptual stage, but the principle has to do with the fact that movement of charged gases is similar to the flow of electrons through a wire.

With support from the Office of High Speed Transportation, Dr. Foa has constructed a 2,000-foot tunnel to test his models. "Flights" of the models are being made to obtain information on propulsion and aerodynamics.

One of the propulsion methods being tested is a development of Dr. Foa's. Basically, it involves the *ejection of whirling air jets*. These form a vortex, or whirlpool, at the rear of the vehicle. The result is high velocity streams of air spiraling

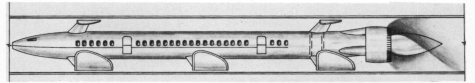

*A
Magnetogasdynamic
Propulsion
Scheme*

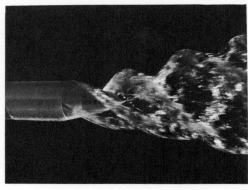

around the vehicle, and dragging the resisting masses of air along with them.

A drawing of such a propulsion scheme is shown, along with an actual photo of the fluid-bladed fan or propeller. In the photo, water has been used as the fluid to provide "visibility."

While current efforts are directed toward the 350-400 mph range, higher speeds are also possible, although they may require yet more futuristic propulsion schemes. Celestial Research, Inc., proposes a system in which the tube vehicle would operate in an atmosphere of saturated water vapor. The idea is to get around the aerodynamic drag problem by condensing the vapor in front of the craft, thus shrinking the vapor and making it easier to get it out of the way. The liquid is then evaporated again at the rear. In this process, it expands and drives the vehicle forward.

64

Which, if any, of these systems eventually becomes operational depends upon the outcome of many studies now in progress. An advantage in all of them (where air or vapor is used in a tube) shows up in the braking process. Clearly, this is an important factor in a craft traveling several hundred miles an hour. In Tubeflight, no sooner is power to the engine shut off than the "piston" characteristic mentioned earlier comes to our aid. That is, the craft rapidly piles up air in front of it and slows down. At high speeds, the action is very rapid. Once the speed has been reduced to a low enough point, conventional friction forces can bring the vehicle to a stop.

Nevertheless, for really high speeds, and for other reasons that will become clear shortly, evacuation of the entire tube (creating a vacuum) must be considered. Probably the most comprehensive system yet proposed is that of L. K. Edwards. Indeed, this is essentially the *gravity-vacuum system* Andrew Mann used for his trip to Oakland in our Prologue.

We begin our discussion of the proposal by looking first at the vacuum aspect. Edwards points out that drag forces due to air resistance, even at present day railroad speeds, are considerable, and that they increase as the square of the speed. At aircraft speeds, the movement of the air in a tube becomes prohibitive. (Even though the air in the Foa system is being used for propulsion, it is still moving from front to rear. The evaporation system is still purely theoretical.)

"Given the requirement for external power plants to remove the air from the tube," says Edwards, "why not make these the sole source of propulsive power for the train?"

It is only necessary to admit air at normal pressure behind the train by a system of valves. The higher pressure will force the train to move forward toward the region of lower pressure.

Toward the end of the trip, it is only necessary to reverse the procedure—that is, to admit air in front of the train, to make it slow down.

There are several interesting differences between this system and those described earlier. For one thing, the concept of streamlining goes right out the window. The simplest and most efficient design calls for the front and back of the train to be perfectly flat, as shown. When sea-level pressure is applied to the roughly 10,000 square inches of either end of the train, a total propulsive (or braking) force of 140,000 pounds, or 70 tons, results. At 50 mph, this matches the pulling power of five large locomotives, and provides ample acceleration capability.

Air can continue to push with this force at speeds as great as 200 mph. "At this point," says Edwards, "the effective power is 70,000 horsepower." Yet the only power plant required for a 450-mile Northeast Corridor system is a bank of four 2,500 hp (horse power) electric motors at one or two point along the tube—a maximum of 20,000 hp.

How can this be? Are we finally getting something for nothing? Not at all, for the motors are working continuously, while the train is only being accelerated for about two minutes.

This is the principle of the *pneumatic catapult*. Energy produced by a low horsepower engine and compressor is stored over a period of time for release in seconds.

In a sense then, reports Edwards, the tube train will be the world's longest catapult. However, the acceleration, instead of being very rapid, will be quite gradual. As a matter of fact, passenger won't even need seat belts. The acceleration will be carefully controlled by a series of valves that will open and close as the train passes through the tunnel.

66

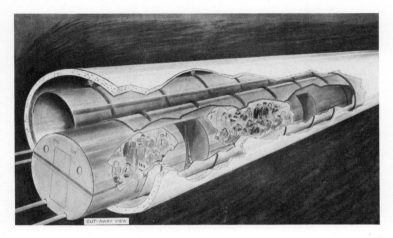

Gravity Vacuum Transit System

The use of pneumatic systems is not new. Pneumatic delivery tubes were once widely used in department stores. They are still in use in large libraries and various other institutions, such as the Paris post office system. A pneumatic passenger system was actually built in Ireland as far back as 1840. But the materials available were not up to the job. A long leather flap, used to seal the long slot by means of which propulsion was accomplished, fell victim to the weather and to rats!

New York City's first subway, built in 1870 and a block long, was of the pneumatic type. A blower propelled the 18-passenger test car through the tunnel in one direction, and then reversed to "suck" it back. It was tested for a whole year and was a popular attraction all the while. But a full size system was never built. The elevated railroads got the nod and became the standard for a number of years.

While Edward's propulsion system is still far in advance

of anything we have now, his suspension system is even more surprising. He suggests the use of steel wheels and rails! His feeling, which is supported by Dr. Ronan, is that this system is the most efficient of all the ones considered so far.

For example, steel wheels moving on steel rails encounter far less resistance than rubber tires rolling and flexing on pavement. It takes $7\frac{1}{2}$ times more force to move a loaded vehicle with rubber tires than it does to move an equally loaded steel-wheeled railroad car. The more advanced systems such as air and magnetic suspension require a continual, additional expenditure of power.

Edwards also says (in clear disagreement with prevailing opinion) that steel wheels will work quite well at speeds up to 500 mph—with some precautions and special adaptation, such as the use of a specially-designed floated tube. It is also worth recalling that jet-propelled autos, traveling on the Bonneville Salt Flats, have attained speeds of more than 600 mph—with rubber tires!

Tunnels

Although a surface tube would work as well as a tunnel, Edwards suggests the latter, for several reasons. He says that a tube on or above the surface would be an "unsightly nuisance." He adds that a reasonable degree of straightness would call for many bridges and tunnels.

The Japanese system, for instance, includes some 40 miles of tunnels. This is a full eighth of its total length, although it is supposed to be a surface system. Since the tube system is intended for downtown-to-downtown trips, some portion of it would have to be underground anyway.

Furthermore, tunneling does not, or need not, disrupt surface activities in congested areas. Bores can be run below the network of water mains, power lines, sewers, and building foundations, eliminating the need for expensive and time-consuming detours. Work in underground facilities progresses steadily in all seasons (below a certain depth the temperature is always above freezing), and in all kinds of weather.

There is yet another reason, at least in the Edwards system. In addition to having his train used in a Corridor-type system, i.e., for medium and long distances, Edwards would also like to see it used for urban transportation. However, while his pneumatic system (which could be put in a surface tube) would work for the former application, it would not suffice for the latter. That is, for shorter trips and heavier, longer trains, pneumatic power alone could not provide the acceleration required. Nor could it, apparently, for speeds above 200 mph, even in the longer distance applications.

We mentioned earlier that the Montreal Metro uses gravity to aid in accelerating its trains. Edwards proposes to obtain similar "free speed" in a similar manner, though on a much larger scale. Clearly, such a system can only operate in tunnels.

Edwards points out that once the decision is made to put the system into a tunnel, it would cost very little more to slope the sides downward on both sides of each station. If the slope is steep enough, e.g., a maximum depth of 4300 feet for an eight mile distance, the trip—using gravity alone!—would take 2.1 minutes. The vehicle, in other words, would act like the bob of a pendulum. In the absence of any frictional forces, the vehicle could swing back and forth between the stations forever.

A passenger in such a train would feel absolutely no front-to-back acceleration; he could stand up and even pour water with no trouble at all. There would be a small feeling of vertical acceleration, which would be similar to but far less than that experienced on a roller coaster. Nevertheless, such a slope would be too steep near the stations for a practical system. Hence the slope is smoothed out or flattened at the ends. The maximum depth of the tunnel then becomes 3,000 feet and, with pneumatic propulsion, the trip takes 3.2 minutes.

Returning now to long-distance transportation, a very curious effect is seen to arise. Suppose we *could* bore a hole straight through the center of the earth and out the other side. And suppose we dropped a rock down the hole. What would happen?

The rock would start off with zero speed and maximum acceleration, or 32 feet per second per second. As it fell, the speed of the rock would increase, but at a continually diminishing rate; for with each foot of fall, there is less of the earth attracting it from the front and more attracting it from the rear.

By the time it reached the center of the earth, the speed of the rock would be at a maximum (about five miles per *second*). But its acceleration would be zero, for now the gravitational attraction in front and back would balance. As it sped through the center point, conditions would reverse. Now there would be more of the earth behind it than in front, and it would begin to slow up. By the time it reached the other side, its speed would be exactly zero mph once again.

Total elapsed time for the trip: 42 minutes. Energy expended: none.

Now, assuming no one caught the stone, back it would go.

Forty-two minutes later, it would appear on our side of the earth again.

The point, of course, is that the hole could be a tunnel and the stone could be a vehicle. We could load the vehicle with 10,000 people or as many tons of cargo. The trip would take the same time and our cost for energy would be no greater.

Total elapsed time for the round trip is a little more than 84 minutes, or just about the time it takes an astronaut traveling at 18,000 mph to circle the earth! This is not a coincidence. Multiply the speed of the stone at the center of the earth by 3,600 (to convert miles per second to mph) and you have a speed of 18,000 mph! This is the speed at which a satellite must be fired horizontally to give it a circular orbit around the earth, just above its surface. (We are, of course, ignoring the effects of air resistance.)

If the satellite (or passenger rocket) is fired off at a higher speed, away it goes into space. So the fastest time one could make in going halfway around the world in this manner is 42 minutes—at an enormous expenditure of fuel.

If, however, we could build our tunnel through the earth, we could get there with no expenditure of energy. If we are in a great rush, all we need do is use some form of propulsion to accelerate us during the first half of our trip. A small, constant acceleration during this period would cut the time considerably. However, the vehicle would then have to be slowed down artificially during the second half. With this technique, we could conceivably make the trip in ten or fifteen minutes.

Will the earth one day be criss-crossed with tunnels like those of earthworms under a lawn? Perhaps. But there are a few small problems that must be solved first. One is a fiery heat at great depths. Another is air resistance, but that could be overcome if the air is removed from the tunnel.

There is also a pressure problem. A vertical, square-inch "rod" of atmosphere weighs about 15 pounds. This is the cause of our atmospheric pressure of 15 pounds per square inch. You have undoubtedly felt the pressure buildup on your eardrums as you dove down into water only ten feet deep. This is simply the weight of the water above you.

As one moves down farther into the earth, the pressure builds up rapidly. At very high pressures, strange things begin to happen. At a pressure of 150,000 pounds per square inch, graphite—black, soft, and greasy—changes to diamond.

Unfortunately, the pressure at the center of the earth is yet 300 times higher. Diamond changes *back* to a soft material. Indeed, any known substance turns into a kind of thick liquid. This is the consistency of the earth's core and is not exactly suited to building material. But there is one thing I have learned in writing this book, and that is *not* to say that something can't be done.

Suppose we didn't have anyone we wanted to visit directly opposite us. Suppose we wished, instead, to go only a quarter of the way around (or through) the earth, say to England. What is the situation then?

Of course, the heat and pressure are cut considerably. But will we still get a free ride? Yes, but now it is more like traveling down an incline than falling down a straight vertical tube. Gravity still acts to pull the vehicle toward the midpoint of the tunnel, although with proportionately less force. So, while we are traveling a shorter distance, we are moving at a slower speed. The result is that the time of the trip remains the same, i.e., 42 minutes.

Indeed, theoretically the time for a free trip through a straight tube to any place on earth is 42 minutes. (For short trips, this figure can be lowered by means of a sloped tunnel, as in the Edwards system.)

Tunneling Techniques

Oddly, cutting a perfectly straight tunnel has long been a major problem. There are no rulers or straight edges that can be counted on for long distances. A pinpoint of light can be used, but the light spreads and so the accuracy of the method is not great. Laser light, however, spreads very little. It is interesting to note that one of the first successful applications of the laser has been in drilling a straight tunnel. The giant tunnel borer shown on the next page maintains arrow straightness with a unique laser-beam guidance system. So we have one of the problems licked.

A different problem is that of cutting through hard materials. The laser may just prove useful here, too. Experiments have shown that bursts of laser light weaken rock to a point where it can practically be dug out like soil. However, the power required thus far is very high.

Compare this to the ancient Roman method, which was quite similar in principle. One of their tunnels was cut through 3,000 feet of solid rock. To do this, they first heated the rock with fire, then doused it with cold water to make it split. Finally, they hacked away at it with hand tools.

Other approaches, aside from the brute force methods of drilling, cutting, and blasting, are also being investigated. Among them are 1) *flame jets*, currently being used in quar-

A Laser Tunnel Borer

ries and taconite mines; 2) high-pressure *water jets* (after all, water did cut the Grand Canyon); and 3) *chemicals:* a substantial weakening of rock samples has been achieved with the application of relatively inexpensive chemical agents.

The study of tunneling techniques is considered an important part of the government's research program. One hope, incidentally, is that the costs of tunnels can be shared. The Post Office is already interested and freight, too, can be shipped this way, perhaps in odd hours. In addition, the outer shell of the tunnel can be used for the transportation of petroleum products, water and/or chemicals.

As a matter of fact, new techniques have been developed for transporting solid materials through pipelines as well. All of this could be combined, with the various users sharing the admittedly high cost of a tunnel. The Office of High Speed Ground Transportation is studying the feasibility of such a multi-use transportation and utility tunnel along the Northeast Corridor.

One more point: energy will be the key to our technological future, as it has been to our past and present. Vast amounts of energy will have to be "shipped" from place to place as energy requirements continue to increase. What more logical way is there than through our tunnel?

A report to Congress on the progress being made in the Corridor program points out that the first work in new technologies has been primarily in three areas: tube vehicles, tunneling, and electrical propulsion. It is also stated that tunnels are sure to be important to any future ground transportation system, not only for the reasons we have given, but also because the cost of surface routes through urban centers is already in some cases above the cost of tunneling. (A proposed 1.2 mile highway across lower Manhattan will cost over $100 million.)

Finally, the Greek city planner Constantinos Doxiados believes that the pressure of expanding population may force us to place the whole system of mechanical transportation underground. Thus, the surface of the earth will be left free for people once again.

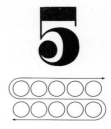

5

The Road Ahead

IN THE DAYS when the railroad was king, many cities literally grew up around the stations. This made sense since railroads, the only fast and reliable means of transportation, were practically the lifelines of the cities. There was no traffic problem, since trains rode on exclusive rights-of-way.

When the automobile came into being, it was "logical" for the highways—which grew out of local roads—to follow the pattern: to run smack through the hearts of the cities. It was not so very long ago that an automobile driver traveling from New York City to Washington, D.C., found himself passing right through the city of Baltimore over a narrow "main" road packed with cars, buses, and trucks. Although the poor driver had no interest in entering Baltimore, he was forced to do so and to fight his way through all kinds of local traffic to boot. (Nationwide traffic studies show that 60 to 80 per cent of all motorists using downtown streets during rush hours don't want to be there at all.)

In other words, an approach that worked when there were

few cars became worse than useless with the fantastic and unexpected rise in auto travel. On the other hand, it is tempting to blame the *whole* problem of city congestion on the automobile. This would be unfair.

For example, the two views on page 79 of a busy Chicago intersection were made in 1910 and 1966. The apparent unconcern of the police officers in the first picture (arrows) suggests that what looks to us like a major traffic tieup was not an unusual occurrence. Yet the automobile is nowhere to be seen.

As long ago as the days of ancient Rome, city traffic was a problem. Julius Caesar was forced to ban wheeled vehicles from the center of that city during the day because of congestion.

In London, the expression "traffic is grinding to a halt" has been heard for a century, and perhaps several centuries. Even the noise problem associated with transportation is not necessarily worse than it once was. Iron-bound wooden wheels bouncing on cobblestone streets assailed one's ears no less than one's insides.

While opinion varies as to whether conditions are worse now than they were before, all agree they are bad enough for something to be done. A point worth noting is that worldwide production of motor vehicles is increasing three times faster than the increase in human population. So things are bound to get worse unless something *is* done.

Modern technology has been, and is being, brought to bear and solutions are appearing. Clearly, the overall problem is large enough and complex enough that no one solution, such as better transit systems, can be expected to do the job.

* * *

Bypassing the City

One very successful approach has been to simply bypass the problem; that is, to put an *expressway* around or alongside the city. The New Jersey Turnpike, a major link in the New York–Washington trip, simply bypasses Newark, Trenton, Philadelphia, and Wilmington along the way. Indeed, a driver can travel the full Turnpike distance without being stopped by a single traffic light.

For travel in and around the individual city, a slightly different approach is taken. While the shortest distance between opposite edges of a city may be a straight line, where traffic is concerned the shortest trip may well be a curved one.

For example, one can now swing around Baltimore on a fine new "Beltway" that encircles the city. A number of other cities (among them, Washington, Boston, and San Diego) have tried the *beltway* idea, and with great success; some use, or will use, more than one at varying distances from the CBD. Thus, people who don't want to enter the downtown area don't have to; they can travel around it.

Boston's beltway, Route 128, is a 65-mile circumferential highway that cuts through rural areas about ten miles from the CBD. It provides easy access to a number of communities in the metropolitan area. It has been a huge commercial success as well, having stimulated a great deal of industrial development. Oddly enough, the area, in spite of its closeness to the city, had defied development for three hundred years. Yet Route 128 had hardly been opened before great industrial and research establishments began to mushroom along the way.

Manhattan, however, is an island. There is no rural land

DEARBORN
and
RANDOLPH
STREETS
CHICAGO, 1910

Two Views of a Chicago Intersection

through which a road can be cut. The highway presently swinging around the island is a four- to six-lane highway which is sadly inadequate for its job. City planners have been trying for years to cut an expressway through the city, but the cost, and the cries of those who would have to be dispossessed in the process, have always prevailed. Now, it appears, the job may finally be done—at a cost of about $100 million for a 1.2 mile highway. To help put this amount of money in perspective, let us note that $3 million will build a 100-bed hospital or a university library.

Still, there is no question that it must be done if the city is not to strangle completely. As matters now stand, a large part of the traffic passing between New Jersey and Queens or Long Island, as well as between the east and west sides of Manhattan, crawls right through the agitated heart of the great city.

J. J. Cummings of the Automobile Manufacturers Association maintains, "Every city that has built even a portion of its planned freeway system already has seen a sharp decline in congestion on its surface streets and a marked increase in peak-hour and off-peak travel speeds on both the freeways and the surface streets."

Furthermore, Mr. Cummings points out that *freeways*, in spite of the higher speed involved, have a safety record three times as good as conventional city streets.

Freeways are especially important in metropolitan areas, and serve two main functions. The first and most obvious is that of providing rapid and convenient accessibility between different parts of the metropolitan region and between regions. But equally important is the fact that they separate through from local traffic. It is this mixture that has traditionally been the explosive one. Thus, we can see the logic to building a freeway alongside a perfectly good road that (sometimes) is not crowded.

The first freeway worth talking about, the Bronx River Parkway north of New York City, was built more than forty years ago. Most freeway development, however, has occurred only in the last two decades.

The expressway, or freeway, is a road specially designed to move large volumes of traffic safely at high speeds. The biggest difference between the freeway and the normal street is the controlled-access feature of the freeway.

Specially designed ramps permit traffic to enter and leave the road only at designated points. So-called "acceleration lanes" give entering cars a chance to get up to speed so that they can merge with the moving traffic easily and safely. Cars leaving the freeway have special lanes that enable them to slow down gradually before turning off. Over- and underpasses eliminate intersections, one of the worst traffic hazards. Median strips divide opposing lanes of traffic. Pedestrians and parking are barred.

However, the idyllic picture we have painted does not hold everywhere. Indeed, the 50-mile Long Island Expressway running out of New York City has scornfully been called "the world's longest parking lot."

A number of suggestions have been made to alleviate the situation. Among them are: building a monorail or express bus lane along the present roadway, building another expressway, double-decking the present one, and charging drivers for the privilege of entering the city by car (unless they can prove they need it). Some humorists suggest closing down Long Island.

Automating the Highway

Another possibility for the future is to automate the highway. This exciting development is usually thought of as a matter of convenience for the driver—a way of allowing him to relax while computers and other electronic devices do the work. *Convenience* is certainly one good reason for developing an automated highway. But there are other, even better, inducements.

A second reason is *safety*. Man is a thoroughly unpredictable animal; while that is his strength in some ways, it is a dangerous trait on the highways. He also has a tendency to fall asleep or to allow his attention to wander when tired or bored. While driving can be fun on local country roads, turnpike driving rarely is; the usual objective is simply to get to the destination in the shortest possible time.

The third argument for automation is perhaps a surprising one, for it is tied in with an unexpected cause of congestion on roads. It is not so much the cars that make the trouble; it is the *spaces* between them! For each ten miles per hour of speed, the safe driver leaves a full car-length of distance between his car and the one in front of him. Using approximate numbers, we can see that, at 20 mph, a 20-foot car uses up 60 feet of highway (20 feet for the car and 40 feet for spacing). Under these conditions, the roadway will (ideally) carry 1,800 cars past a set point per hour.

At 60 mph, each car requires a block 140 feet long. But, because the cars are traveling faster, more will pass the set point in unit time and the highway capacity rises—theo-

An Automated Highway

retically. However, slow drivers, lane-changers, and other "trouble makers" keep the figure somewhere between 1,500 and 2,000 cars per hour.

Thus, we can increase the capacity of the roadway in two ways: increase the speed of the cars, and decrease the spacing. With man at the wheel, neither solution is a wise one. With electronics, both are possible.

A few years ago, a continuous guidance cable was buried in an oval track in southern New Jersey. Additional electronic equipment was placed as needed. On the road were two cars equipped with special controls and passengers, but no drivers.

The cars were steered, accelerated, and braked automatically. The passengers were informed of "hazards" and mythical intersections via the car radio. The information came from the guidance cable.

With automatic control, spacing can be cut down considerably, immediately doubling or tripling the capacity of the road. Even in so simple a matter as braking in an emergency, machines not only don't fall asleep, but they also react much faster than humans. It takes an alert driver about a second before he even begins to apply the brake after seeing trouble. At sixty miles an hour, his car will travel 88 feet before the brakes even begin to work. A great deal can happen in 88 feet.

It is no surprise that multiple rear-end collisions are a frequent occurrence. One such accident actually involved 200 cars, when drivers on a turnpike apparently misjudged visibility and maintained too close a headway! Machines can apply the brakes immediately.

Even so, will motorists allow control of their cars to be taken away from them? They may well balk at first. Some proposals, therefore, include a "stepped" plan. L. E. Flory of Radio Corporation of America, who was involved in the automatic highway development just discussed, suggests the following set of steps:

1) Better ways of informing the driver, so that he can make better and faster decisions.

2) An over-ride system, whereby the equipment takes over if the driver does not respond to warnings or an emergency situation in time.

3) A completely automated control system.

The roadway might eventually look like that shown here.

"AUTOLINE"- - - *Automatic Highway Concept*

1 A motorist traveling in a normal lane but wanting to enter the Autoline lane would move into the transition lane and signal his desire to enter the Autoline.

2 By putting his car on automatic control, his speed and position would be monitored and adjusted.

3 The car would be automatically guided into position at the end of the first available group on the Autoline lane.

4 To leave the Autoline lane, the motorist would first signal his intention to the system.

5 His car would move automatically into the transition lane at the first safe opportunity.

6 He would return his car to manual control and then move into a normal lane.

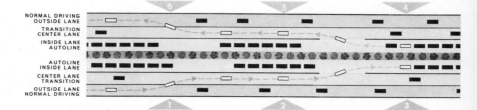

NORMAL DRIVING
OUTSIDE LANE
TRANSITION
CENTER LANE
INSIDE LANE
AUTOLINE

AUTOLINE
INSIDE LANE
CENTER LANE
TRANSITION
OUTSIDE LANE
NORMAL DRIVING

General Motor's Automated "Autoline"

The outer lanes in each direction are normal, non-automated lanes. The middle lanes in each direction serve for both passing and transition, if desired, to automatic control. At specified points, the driver would signal the system that he wishes to enter. It might be possible at this point for a quick, automatic check to be made of the condition of the vehicle, similar to that now done on spacecraft before blast-off.

Assuming all is well, control would then be taken over by the system and the vehicle would be guided into the first available empty space in the inner lane. Here cars are spaced evenly, but relatively close together. To get off the roadway, the driver reverses the procedure.

General Motors estimates that groups of vehicles could

cruise safely at 70 mph on this Autoline, giving a capacity of 9,000 vehicles per hour—the equivalent of six normal lanes of traffic. A similar system in which cars are hooked to each other is shown.

Some transportation experts see the beginning of automated systems in use within the next two to fifteen years, in spite of the fact that it might add as much as $500 onto the cost of a car. However, Federal Highway Administrator Lowell Bridwell figures that fully automated expressways are at least twenty-five years away.

Let us see what kind of developments we can expect in the meantime. One is a possible gradual rise in speeds along the major expressways.

An Automated Highway "Convoy" System

Cornell Aeronautical Laboratory, which is actively engaged in transportation studies, envisions the *Century Expressway*, a non-automatic highway that would be capable of accommodating cruising speeds of 100 miles per hour or more. A second phase, looking toward speeds of about 150 mph, would require some form of guideway/vehicle combination that does not depend upon the friction of tires on pavement for maintaining stability and control.

Perhaps one or more of the techniques we have already discussed for guiding trains, such as fluid or magnetic systems, will be used. In any case, it seems clear that such an expressway would be available only to a special class of drivers with a special class of vehicles. Possibly both driver and vehicle would be tested before entry was permitted.

Certainly, careful monitoring of the highway would be required. Modern developments in electronics and computers will make this relatively easy. Experiments are already being carried out on control of expressways based on *television monitoring*.

In Detroit, for instance, the flow of traffic is surveyed continuously by fourteen television cameras spaced at quarter-mile intervals. When a "critical density" of traffic has built up, entrance ramps to that section are closed! Traffic is diverted through alternate routes to the next open ramp. This may be a little rough on a few drivers, but on balance, all drivers benefit. A recent study by Michigan State University showed that average speed has increased from 27 to 37 mph, traffic volume has *increased* five to ten per cent, and traffic tieups have been cut considerably.

On Chicago's Congress Street Expressway, the intermediate television step is bypassed completely. Monitoring is done entirely with *electronic sensors.* The results are fed into a computer that closes ramps automatically by activating signals directing traffic to other routes. Obviously, such monitoring techniques could be applied for high-speed routes as well.

Providing the driver with the information he needs for intelligent driving and navigating is another area where we can expect some improvement. There is no technical reason why drivers cannot be warned somehow of impending danger, congestion, or other conditions ahead, so that he can take appropriate action early enough to avoid the difficulty. Some roads already have warning signs which indicate ice, fog, or other general conditions.

This could be carried much further. It might be possible, for example, to provide *remote control lane-changers,* so that drivers do not come upon stopped vehicles so suddenly and unexpectedly that they cannot do anything about it.

In addition to these obvious advantages, a flexible sign system might be useful in other ways. For example, in order to control and meter efficiently the merging of vehicles on high-speed roads and thereby obtain higher capacity, it is necessary to utilize gaps in the main stream as they occur. The heart of such a system is *a gap-measuring device and computer*—both of which are already available.

In effect, the holes in the traffic stream are measured and their speed computed. A vehicle entering a ramp can then be given instructions as to the speed that must be attained in order to meet the gap when it arrives at the merging point. This is very important at high speeds.

The signals to the ramp vehicle will, at least initially, be variable signs which will provide start, speed, and merge information at the appropriate times. The basic logic for the development of this system has already been completed and the development of hardware (actual computer equipment) begun.

Once a vehicle is traveling at high speed, however, there is a very strict limit to how much information can be supplied to the driver by signs. This is particularly true at night, or during a long trip when drivers are typically less alert. The Federal Highway Administration is looking into the possibility of developing a system of communications that would link the driver's radio with recorded or spoken messages wherever needed.

Another category of improvement has to do with improved methods for more rapid and efficient removal of obstructions, such as accidents and stalled vehicles, from the roadway. Often, the roadway blocks up so rapidly behind the problem area that a tow truck must crawl along at a snail's pace to get to the spot. Sometimes it must even approach from the opposite direction and then, if there is a median barrier, find some way to cross it.

One approach that has been tried experimentally is to use a helicopter to move or remove the obstruction. While there is no doubt that this works, it is an expensive approach and has not been adopted as an operational method as yet.

Highways Underground

If, as city planner Constantinos Doxiados says, all metropolitan surface transportation must eventually go underground, this problem may be solved more easily. George A. Hoffman, of the University of California, has proposed a system of deep tunnels and parking areas as a solution to the present and future ills of the city. Traffic would be carried through tunnels dug by means of the modern techniques we have already discussed. At the same time, there would be, overhead, electrified rails on which police and aid vehicles could travel at high speed above jammed lanes. Electrically driven capsules, containing patrolmen well-versed in first aid and fully equipped with ladders, grappling apparatus, and medical supplies, would quickly reach a disabled vehicle, render any medical assistance required, and lift or tow the vehicle out of the way by means of a telescoping crane. A vast system of underground parking spaces is also proposed as an answer to the city parking problem.

Such ideas may be closer to reality than you think. The Dallas, Texas, City Council is working on a long-range transportation plan to serve the CBD up to the year 2000. Major items in the plan are:

1) A huge downtown transportation terminal
2) Doubled parking capacity in the CBD
3) Gradual conversion of Main Street to a pedestrian mall; two lanes would be reserved for buses and emergency vehicles
4) A $15 million, 1¼-mile truck tunnel under Main Street.

Of course, on the scale envisioned by Hoffman, fumes emitted by the passage of thousands of vehicles in an enclosed space would present a terrible problem. Yet he feels that the problem is by no means insurmountable. He even suggests that an enterprising company might be able to tap the system's exhaust stacks. Thus, at one stroke, the gases injected into the atmosphere would be purified, and a substantial amount of unburned hydrocarbons (fuel in gaseous form) could be recovered and sold.

There is still another way to approach the fume problem that exists above ground as well as below, and that is not to generate any in the first place. We'll talk about that in the next chapter.

6

The Electric Car
and the City Center

EVEN above ground, in the open air, air pollution is now recognized as a serious threat to health, as well as a destructive force to crops and buildings. Automobiles are identified as a major, though not the only, offender. Laws have been passed requiring that measures be taken by automobile manufacturers to cut down on the pollutants emitted in the exhausts of their cars. Some progress has been made.

However, the number of cars and trucks is increasing so rapidly that the progress made is rapidly eaten up by the increasing number of emitters. Almost 80 million cars are now on American roads, about one for every 2.5 persons in the country, not to speak of trucks and buses. The figure is expected to reach 200 million by the year 2000. That's nearly three times today's number and almost one car for each adult.

Many people feel that a more direct approach to the air

pollution problem is needed. Few doubt that this more direct approach is the electric car.

The electric car is not a new idea. The first "practical" electric vehicle was built 'way back in 1837, fully half a century before the equivalent gasoline-powered car was built.

But once the latter vehicle appeared, improvements in the gasoline-powered motor, the so-called internal combustion engine, were so rapid and so significant that it rapidly outstripped the battery as a provider of power. The gasoline-powered car became lighter, more powerful, and could travel considerably longer between service stops. This is still true. A car can make 200-250 miles on one tank of gasoline. Modern electrics are limited to perhaps 50 miles per battery charge—under good conditions.

As long as there weren't too many cars on the road, these were telling advantages, and the electric car gave way. Yet the features of the electric vehicle were there, and such vehicles have been around right along. In England, where gasoline is more expensive than it is here, there are estimated to be some 100,000 electric vehicles in use, mainly in the form of delivery vans.

Electric vehicles are used in the United States, too, but are mostly found in the form of golf carts (which are being used for street travel in a few areas on the West Coast) and transporters used in large factories. The emission-free operation of electrics explains the second use, and the convenient, efficient operation in low-speed, stop-and-go applications explains the first.

It must be kept in mind that a gasoline engine is burning a considerable amount of fuel even when it is standing still, as when the engine is idling. In the electric car, on the other hand, there is no drain on the battery when the car is stopped. It's like turning off a flashlight.

The Automobile Manufacturers Association reports that 60 per cent of car trips are less than five miles in length (going to the supermarket, the movies, bowling, and so on). And 50 per cent of the use of cars is for going to and from work. Here, the average length of the trip is six to ten miles. Over half the cars contain only the driver!

Is an 18-foot, 300-horsepower, two-ton fume-spitter really necessary for this kind of traveling? More and more the answer seems to be, "No."

No one claims that the automobile as we know it today is on the way out, or even that it should be. Certainly, for inter-city and inter-metropolitan driving at 60 to 80 mph along today's marvelous superhighways, and for comfort and convenience, it is a pleasure indeed. Time will bring even further refinements, improvements, new designs, even new power plants. Cars may even become more luxurious than they are today. The photo shows a prototype of an experimental station wagon built by the Ford Motor Company.

But on the local streets, where more and more cars are fighting for space, where travel is typically at 20 to 25 mph and no more than 30 to 50 miles per day, a different approach is necessary. The small, agile, easily parked electric car certainly seems to be one good answer. Many experimental vehicles have already been built and are running.

Of course, electric cars should be easy to charge. It is already possible to charge them by plugging into a home outlet. Another possibility is illustrated on page 96: namely, metered charging when the car is parked at a meter.

At the moment, almost daily recharging is necessary (de-

Ford's Station Wagon of Tomorrow

pending, of course, on the distances and severity of the driving). Although it is a simple matter, it does take a few hours at least and people are prone to be forgetful. One possibility is to have some kind of automatic recharging take place whenever the car is driven into a garage or driveway.

In the more distant future, this kind of problem will no longer exist. An experimental vehicle has already been built which can find its way down a corridor by bouncing radio signals off the walls. When batteries need charging, the device seeks out the nearest electric outlet and plugs in.

If electrics really become popular, many service stations will go out of business. For those of us who have been lucky

95

*Meter for
Recharging
an
Electric Car*

enough to be near a station when we had car trouble, this will
be recognized as a considerable disadvantage. But electrics
are much simpler and more reliable. They are less likely to
cause trouble, and so the situation may balance out, after all.

On the other hand, the question of convenience may turn
out to be quite irrelevant. Research chemist Donald E. Carr
maintains that the electric auto is the *only* hope for stopping
the otherwise inevitable asphyxiation of our cities.

Since the United States is becoming more and more a two-
car-family nation, many families will be able to own at least
one electric, while still having available a larger and more
luxurious car. Yet there will always be those who do not want
or cannot afford two cars. How about them? Must they buy
a large, gasoline-engine car and perhaps eventually be barred

96

from the city altogether? Or must they buy a small electric with its admittedly limited performance?

It is unlikely that this uncomfortable choice will have to be made for very long. Ford, for example, is working on a hybrid vehicle which would run on batteries in metropolitan areas and switch to gasoline power when out on the open road. The batteries would automatically be charged when the car is running in the latter mode.

Several other possibilities present themselves. It is just possible that the car manufacturers will be able to develop a fume-free, or almost fume-free, car, perhaps in the form of the still-being-developed gas turbine automobile. The turbine engine runs on inexpensive kerosene or fuel oil, requires no carburetor, no piston rings, no radiator, and only one spark plug. As another possibility, we might even return to the steam engine!

It is even more likely that the vast range of experiment and experience in the battery-driven motor and appliance field (e.g., razors, toothbrushes, carving knives, golf carts, etc.) will lead to electric sources that can provide the performance we expect from present-day autos.

New Sources of Power

Various types of battery systems are under development. One or more of these may provide the higher performance being sought—at a reasonable price.

A *silver-zinc battery* has already been developed which has five times the energy density of the common lead-acid type, but is far higher in price. A *sodium-sulphur battery* is fifteen times more efficient, but must operate at more than 500°F, creating a potentially dangerous situation.

It may one day be possible to develop a *nuclear-powered* car. Not only would such a vehicle be pollution-free, but one pound of uranium can do the job of 360,000 gallons of gasoline! At the moment, however, no one has suggested a way to produce a small, low-cost reactor. Other major problems are the initially high cost of the fuel, the requirements for shielding, and the potential danger of radiation released in a crash.

A more likely candidate, at least at present, is the *fuel cell*. Invented back in the 1800's, this is a device that does not employ the discharge-recharge system that batteries require. Instead, it can convert fuel directly and continuously into electricity as long as the fuel is available.

In one form, it uses hydrogen and oxygen to provide electricity (and water). This was the type of system that General Electric developed for use in the Gemini space flights. Fuel cells also provide 3,000 watts of electricity for the Apollo Command Module, along with seventeen quarts of drinkable water each day.

Unfortunately, the fuel cell so far is complex and the fuel is still expensive. The system is still far out of the range of the average motorist. However, the Army is testing a ¾-ton electric truck powered by a 40,000 watt hydrazine-air fuel cell. Results so far indicate that the truck performs as well as, or better than, a standard ¾-ton vehicle powered by a 94-hp internal combustion engine. Army engineers believe that a hydrocarbon fuel, which may give *100 to 150 miles per gallon*, can eventually be used to power the fuel cells.

Another possibility is the use of hydrogen and oxygen in a different way. A common chemical experiment splits water

98

into its component hydrogen and oxygen by means of an electric current, and then "explodes" these gases back into water. Is it possible that this explosion could provide a simpler system than the fuel cell for propelling a fume-free car?

One of the most exciting aspects of the fuel cell is its remarkably high efficiency, theoretically almost 100 per cent. Practical fuel cells have already been operated at 75 per cent efficiency, or three times as high as an internal combustion engine. This outstanding ability to convert chemical energy directly into electricity, rather than having to go through a burning or combustion cycle, explains why fuel cells have already been the subject of so much research and development.

Manfred Altman, of the University of Pennsylvania, foresees the advent of the electric automobile in three distinct steps over a ten-year period. The first generation of such vehicles will be rented from firms that will own and service them, just as larger cars are rented today. The second generation will be an improved version, with a high-enough performance level to begin to attract private ownership on a large scale. Finally, the third step will be high-performance vehicles powered by fuel cells.

Assuming he is right, our air pollution problem will be helped considerably, if not solved. But what about the problem of congestion? Will all cars have to be parked outside the city limits the way Japanese leave their shoes outside the house?

One answer, as we have seen, is to put everything (except pedestrians) underground. Another is to stick with Phase I of Dr. Altman's forecast. For example, Dr. James P. Romualdi, Director of the Transportation Research Institute of the Carnegie Institute of Technology, pictures each suburban family

An Enclosed All-Weather Highway

equipped with a private car, plus a small electric vehicle owned by a regional transportation authority. The commuter, on his way to work, would deliver the car to an office of the authority at his local transit station. That car might be used by several other people during the day, in which case he would simply pick up another car at night which he would drive home.

Others see just the reverse picture. That is, urban and suburban families would own the smaller electric runabouts, and would rent the larger, more powerful cars (perhaps even electric ones) for the few long trips made during the year.

In any case, there is little doubt that electric cars are on their way back. Stewart Udall, Secretary of the Interior, predicts that half the motor vehicles on the road in twenty years will be electrically powered.

Widespread use of electric autos would make possible whole new systems of transportation. For example, many routes could be enclosed, providing all-weather comfort and convenience. Developments in *photochromic* glass and plastic would enable transporterways to darken automatically in strong sunlight, thus giving protection against the sun's glare and perhaps heat. Ways might even be found to utilize the heat absorbed by the darkened material.

New Means of Mobility

Are cars, even electric runabouts, the only answer to greater mobility in and around the city? How about the approach shown here?

As you can see, the *jet-belt* or, as the Bell Aerosystems

people call it, the *Pogo*, is already a reality. Both one- and two-man devices have been successfully flown many times, at speeds up to 60 mph. With one of these parked in your back yard, a trip to the city would be a cinch. And once there, the "vehicle" takes up little enough room. The trip would be a little cold and perhaps wet in the winter, but electrically heated, waterproof clothing would take care of that.

One problem might be that of obtaining fuel, at least at first. Imagine going up to your favorite service station and asking him to "fill-er-up" with nitrogen tetroxide and a 50/50 blend of hydrazine and unsymmetrical dimethylhydrazine. This is the same fuel that is used for the Apollo lunar module.

Indeed, the Pogo has been proposed for use on the moon, where it would be very useful. Fueling the Pogo might be even easier there than at your service station, for hopefully there will be some fuel left in the lunar module tanks.

A range of about 12 miles is seen for the moon application. On earth, with its much higher gravity, this figure is far lower (less than 1,000 feet). Hence the device, so far, is of much greater interest to the military and space establishments than to the average man. Still, there is little doubt that the future will see such devices in use by at least the braver (and richer) among us.

Or how about the long-dreamed-of *personal helicopter?* The cheapest helicopter today runs a smart $25,000, and running and maintenance costs are proportionately high. Of course, as more and more helicopters are manufactured, and with new developments which we take up in Chapter Nine, these costs will undoubtedly come down.

If you don't happen to have $25,000 lying around, but can scrape up 300 feet of clear space for landing and taking off,

Bell's "Pogo" Jet-Belt

The Benson Gyrocopter

perhaps the craft shown on the facing page is a better idea. For just under a thousand dollars, plus some do-it-yourself effort, the Bensen *Gyrocopter* should provide a convenient and exciting form of travel. As a matter of fact, if there is a good wind up, you don't even need the 300 feet of space.

For the less hardy, improving rail or even road travel is a better answer. In the Bowling Green-Bleeker Street line that ran along Broadway in 1825 (Chapter Two), passengers "stopped" the carriage by yanking a cord attached to the driver's leg. Recent developments in electricity and electronics have provided us with somewhat more sophisticated methods for communication between conveyance and passenger. Elevator passengers need only know how to read numbers and push buttons. With certain refinements, this technique could be applied to horizontal travel as well.

For example, it is quite likely that small electric buses, running on frequent schedules, could provide convenient service even in a car-free CBD. Combining this with the principle of the automatic roadway, we have an automatic *Minibus*.

The vehicle could be programmed to stop at passengers' command—from inside by pulling a cord or pushing a button, and from the stations by inserting a coin or token into a signaling device. Or the system might be a free service of the city or business section, in which case it would only be necessary to press a button at the station. In any case, the number of coins, credit cards, or button pushes could be transmitted to a central dispatch point and used for a flexible schedule that would almost guarantee you a seat.

There would, of course, still be a problem of cross traffic (unless the lines were elevated or depressed, in which case we get involved with the additional bother of stairs or escalators). But this is not an impassible barrier even now, particularly in non-congested, bus-only areas. Automatic transporters, called Robotugs, have already been built which follow tapes along the floor of factories. They can be, and have been, programmed to stop and wait for any cross traffic that does occur.

Already in use in several cities is the *Speedwalk passenger conveyor*, which was widely used at the 1964-65 New York World's Fair. At the San Francisco International Airport, two 450-foot-long Speedwalks (rather like horizontal escalators without steps) are taking some of the walking out of flying. Designed to accommodate 7,200 passengers per hour, they link the United Air Lines ticketing area with the airline's flight gate positions.

One problem with moving sidewalks is that they are slow; they *must* be, in order for passengers to get on and off a steadily moving mechanism safely and easily. Trips of any consequence, therefore, would take an inordinately long time.

In our Prologue, Andrew Mann used an intermediate belt. You will recall that when he got off the "glidewalk," he stepped from the moving belt onto a slower one and then finally onto solid ground. Clearly, a series of these belts can be provided so that, by stepping from one to another, almost any final speed can be obtained.

There is a catch, however. A belt safely moving at 240 feet per minute has a speed just over 2.7 mph. This is still slower than a man can walk. In one lovely science-fiction story, "The Roads Must Roll," by Robert Heinlein, the entire transportation system depended on moving roads, the fastest of which traveled at 100 miles per hour. Mr. Heinlein chose to ignore the fact that some thirty-five belts running side by side would have been necessary to get the passenger up to that speed

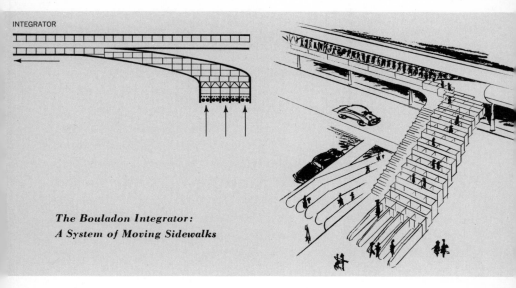

The Bouladon Integrator:
A System of Moving Sidewalks

(that is, if he were not required to be an acrobat getting from one to another).

A most intriguing proposal has recently been made which might be able to overcome this difficult interfacing problem. The Bouladon *Integrator* starts off as a wide multiple escalator. Dividers separate the wide steps into four or five compartments holding two passengers each, and provide hand-holds as well. The escalator moves forward as usual, but also begins to accelerate sideways. Forward motion of each tier of steps stops as the tiers drop into place one behind the other, thus forming a steadily moving glideway. Speeds of 20 mph or more seem perfectly feasible. The procedure is reversed at the destination.

For a series of stations, the compartment door can be opened onto a train or belt, moving parallel to it and at the same speed, during the "high speed" portion of the run. The escalator, once emptied, then reverses the procedure at the next local stop; it drops off any passengers and starts the run once again.

107

Clearly, this is a complex and costly affair. For high density areas, however, the continuous service offered would certainly be superior to anything we have now.

A less complicated arrangement, and one that is already in operation, is that offered by the Goodyear *PeopleMover*. This is a new, fixed-route transportation system in which small cars are used. The cars don't have motors, but the roadway does. Again, continuous, automatic processing of passengers is the objective. The first such system was opened in June of 1967 at the Tomorrowland section of Walt Disney's Disneyland, in California. Made up into 62 four-car trains, the PeopleMover vehicles are propelled by powered rubber wheels.

The cars never stop. They run continuously at speeds ranging from a high of 7 mph down to 1½ mph at boarding and unloading points, where a synchronized, revolving transfer-platform enables passengers to get on and off easily while the cars continue to move. (Incidentally, this saves a great deal of power since it is much harder to get a car moving than to keep it moving.)

By varying the speed of the drive wheels, the system can be programmed to slow or accelerate the cars at precise locations. The system can carry 4,885 passengers per hour over the ¾-mile course, which goes to and through many of the Tomorrowland pavilions.

A variation of this system is being developed for the planned $600 million Disney World—a complete, planned community —in central Florida, and for a $35 million, year-round, outdoor recreational area being designed for the High Sierra of California. Similar systems have been proposed for use in Chicago's Loop and as a replacement for the Times Square-Grand Central Station shuttle in New York.

Developers of the system suggest these other possible applications:

- Helping busy shoppers cover more ground faster and easier in large shopping centers
- Moving students between widely separated buildings on the large, sprawling campuses of large universities
- Carrying passengers to and from parking areas in airports, shopping centers, CBDs, industrial plants and complexes, and sports stadiums.

It is not hard to visualize how such a system might be used in a CBD. The Stephens-Adamson Manufacturing Company of Aurora, Illinois, has proposed a similar car-type passenger system known as the *Carveyor*. Passengers would enter and leave the cars from a moving belt or platform. This technique is similar to the multiple-belt process we discussed earlier, and was used safely and successfully in the General Motors and Ford pavilions at the New York World's Fair.

Cities might construct huge parking lots and garages at the fringes of downtown areas. Expressways would funnel CBD-bound passengers into these parking areas, through which the Carveyor would pass. Loading and unloading stations could be built anywhere along the route through the CBD.

As the cars leave the station, they pass over special conveyors (a variation of the PeopleMover wheels) which cause them to accelerate to 15 mph. As they again approach a station, they are automatically slowed down. Closely spaced "live roll" conveyors move the cars smoothly around curves. Curves and arcs are no problem because of the small size of the individual cars.

A "Carveyor" System

The cars pass through the station end-to-end at the rate
of about 16 vehicles per minute, so that at any one time there
are always cars at the station. The cars seat four to ten passengers; except for extraordinary circumstances, waiting time
would be zero. As the cars move out of the stations, they separate automatically because of the increasing speed.

A Carveyor circuit could take the form of a conventional
double-track system, or the loop arrangement we have already
discussed (page 35). In the illustration, the system is seen
as an overhead one which moves along the outer edge of the
sidewalk. It could also be cantilevered out from the side of
buildings. It could even move through or under buildings or

110

along special routes on the surface. A big advantage is that no signals are required, thus eliminating the need for motor-men and conductors.

Whether such systems will be built and used in CBDs remains to be seen. Until they are, there are simpler, and per-haps unexpected, solutions to the urban travel problem. A few of these are presented in the following chapters.

7

Road/Rail
Systems

My wife and I had been touring Yugoslavia and Greece by car for a month. We had left our two children with my wife's sister who was living in Germany at the time, and were anxious to get back and see them. Our destination was Salzburg, Austria, where we planned to spend the night.

At Spittal, Austria, we had a choice of three routes: 1) 70 miles in one direction over relatively poor, winding mountain roads, 2) 90 miles over somewhat better mountain roads, or 3) 66 miles over fairly good, flat roads.

The third route was made possible by a five-mile tunnel cut through solid rock. Since automobile exhausts would have quickly filled the tunnel to a poisonous level, and air-conditioning would have been a very difficult job in the heart of a mountain, a car-on-train "piggy-back" system is used in the tunnel.

There was little question in our minds. We had already driven several hours that day and looked forward to getting to Salzburg. We drove the 23 miles to the beginning of the tunnel and pulled into line behind other cars. In a few minutes, the train, not much more than a flat car with guides, pulled into the station. We drove onto the train and relaxed. About ten minutes later, we started off through the tunnel. Ten minutes after that, we emerged on the other side, relaxed and refreshed.

On to Salzburg! Time saved: a good hour and a half.

A number of tunnels like this are in use in the more mountainous areas of Europe. While short tunnels can be, and are, used for autos traveling under their own power, longer ones would be very difficult to keep from being contaminated by the engine exhausts. Such railroad/car combination systems may well be prototypes of a development that will become more widespread, and not just in mountainous areas.

One of the advantages of such a system is that it eliminates the old problem of "interfacing" two or more systems—that is, transferring from auto to train, and then back again to rented auto, taxi, bus, or subway at the other end. A trip I once took from a New Jersey town to Boston required, in addition to a one-hour flight, five other transportation modes and an additional three and a quarter hours.

The road/rail system takes advantage of the old adage, "If you can't beat 'em, join 'em." In other words, collection and delivery systems (auto, bus, subway, etc.) are combined with the trunk line.

When, and if, the 32-mile Channel tunnel, which would connect England and France, is built, autos will be carried across the English Channel on double-decked railroad cars in 45 minutes. The trip now takes about two hours by ferry and is normally a very rough crossing; almost universal seasickness is one of the major reasons for a long-standing interest in the project.

It looks at the moment as if the Channel tunnel ("chunnel") is finally going to be built—at a cost of more than $500,000,000! It should be noted, however, that the project has been under discussion for more than two centuries and that digging was actually begun once before, in 1878.

For long-distance travel, of course, remaining in the car would be neither convenient nor comfortable. In a piggy-back system proposed for connecting Jacksonville, Florida, with Washington, D.C., there would be service cars at either end of the 10-car train, offering food, television, even a movie theater. According to the Department of Transportation, the interior will be painted "green, gold and white, blended with warm wood tones."

For those who prefer the privacy of their own vehicles, the cars will be parked with enough space between them for easy access to the trunk and the picnic basket. There will even be large windows in the train cars, to afford good views of the scenery.

The great advantage of the proposed system is that the driver can leave the long-distance driving to the railroad— without losing the convenience of having his own car with him when he arrives. Travelers with young children will perhaps appreciate this most.

Should the system go into operation, it will work something like this: A prospective passenger will make a reservation and pay about $100 for his ticket, or about $75 more than the one-way coach fare. But he will be able to bring along a "reasonable" number of passengers. If four people travel this way, the car rides "free." All told, about 85 autos will be carried on the 15-car train.

For the more distant future, a strange-looking vehicle has been designed. Spanning two sets of tracks, the *RRollway* would permit sideways loading, which would be far more rapid and convenient than the end-on, one-after-another systems now in use. Furthermore, the extremely wide gauge (17½ feet from rail to rail) would provide great stability, making 200 mph speeds quite practicable.

Yet a little thought convinces us that even this technique is far from perfection. One big problem is that of intermediate stops. Traveling at 200 mph, the trip from Washington to Jacksonville would take 3¾ hours. This is fine, if you happen to be leaving from Washington or nearby.

The late Charles Kettering of General Motors once told this story: He was traveling by car in a backwoods section of Kentucky where there were few roads. It wasn't long before he became lost. A little while later, he overtook a resident of the area and asked him how to get to Cincinnati from there.

"Well," the man said, "you go up here to the fork. There you turn left. Let me see. No, I guess you'd better turn right. Well now, to tell you the truth, if I was goin' to Cincinnati, I just wouldn't start from here."

The point, of course, is that we don't want the motorist in Raleigh, North Carolina, to feel that he just shouldn't have started from there if he wanted to take the new railroad to Jacksonville. So we must have intermediate stops. But then another problem arises: if the train were to make ten stops of even a short three minutes apiece, a total of fifty minutes

115

would be added onto the trip. The extra twenty minutes is taken up in slowing down and accelerating for each stop. Average speed is thereby reduced from 200 mph to 166.

Obviously, this is not a problem which is solely restricted to car-carrying trains. It affects all trunkline carriers, indeed all public transportation. The traditional solution is the use of express and local service, with the usual problems of interfacing them and the necessarily slow pace of the locals.

In-Motion Transfers

A better solution is to effect transfer between train and station without requiring the main train (or other vehicle) to stop. This might very well be the greatest advance we can make in our transportation of the future, for it can work in all areas—in long, medium, and short distance travel. There are several ways of accomplishing this.

One basic approach is illustrated in *Figure A*. Passenger-carrying *"capsules"* are exchanged between the through-train and a local which is rapidly brought up to matching speed. It is like handing a ham sandwich from your car window to that of your next-lane neighbor, when and if both speeds could be matched and held. (I don't recommend this, even as a lark. Autos do not have the train's lateral stability, which is provided by the straight rails and flanged wheels. Indeed, precise positioning of trains made possible by this system is one of the reasons why steel wheels are suggested for the gravity-vacuum train.)

With both trains, local and express, "locked" together for a few moments, the capsules could be exchanged with dispatch.

116

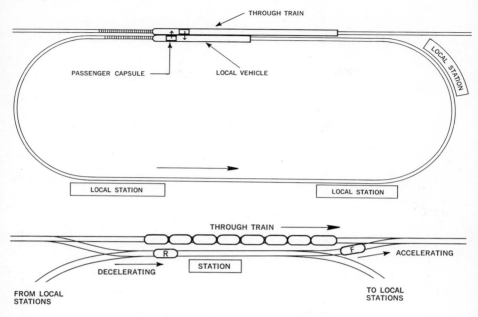

THROUGH TRAIN

PASSENGER CAPSULE

LOCAL VEHICLE

LOCAL STATION

LOCAL STATION

LOCAL STATION

THROUGH TRAIN

R

F

ACCELERATING

DECELERATING

STATION

FROM LOCAL
STATIONS

TO LOCAL
STATIONS

A Passenger-Carrying Exchange System

To the passengers, it might feel like a fast take-off at a traffic light.

An exciting alternative is to transfer *entire train cars.* The process might start by having one or more train cars (pods) waiting in a station. Passengers get on and are seated. At a certain time, determined by computer, the doors close and the self-propelled pod starts moving. As shown in *Figure B*, the pod (*F*) accelerates rapidly and moves out in front of the fast-moving through-train.

This is similar to the docking maneuvers that take place during rendezvous between a space ship and a speeding capsule in orbit. Even though both craft may be zipping along at

117

18,000 mph, an astronaut can step from one to the other exactly as if both craft were standing still. The only requirement is that both craft be traveling the same course and at the same rate of speed. In the train system, the "rendezvous" is accomplished with no loss of time or speed for the through-train.

At the same time, as the train is approaching the station, one or more cars (R) are dropped off the rear of the train and are brought to a stop at the local station. The potential of this system is great because the local vehicle can then become part of the local distribution system. If two cars are dropped, one might go in one direction and the second in another.

Rail-Bus Systems

These local vehicles need not be restricted to tracks. They could, for example, be fitted with rubber tires and moved out into a local, flexible, distribution mode. Thus, the same vehicle might travel 200 mph on the trunk line, 70 mph along a computer-controlled route such as the BART line in the San Francisco area, and, finally, pick up a driver (if necessary) and operate as a conventional bus on local streets.

The remarkable flexibility of such a system (here, for the first time, we have the right to use the word "system") can be illustrated by a more localized example. Let us mark one of our railbuses "New York City," and have it take a morning route through Englewood, New Jersey. At the same time, we will have another such vehicle, also marked "New York City," circulating through Hackensack, New Jersey. After collecting

118

A Highway Interchange for Buses

passengers in their respective cities, the two vehicles pick up the rarely used Erie tracks heading south. While in motion, they meet and couple. The front bus is then designated "Downtown" or "City Hall" and the rear one is marked "Midtown" or "Grand Central."

When the two railbuses couple (convoy grouping), the doors between them are opened and free movement between them becomes possible. The passengers then regroup themselves. The burden of sorting passengers thus falls on them rather than on the system. (Clearly, this is only feasible on an exclusive right-of-way such as a railroad track, or perhaps a bus-only lane. Unexpected stops for other traffic would be very dangerous.)

At Secaucus, the railbuses uncouple; the front vehicle heads for the Lincoln Tunnel. Once on the New York side, it circulates through the midtown area, preferably on bus-only lanes, making several stops along the way. The other railbus continues south, then moves through the Holland Tunnel and circulates in the City Hall area. Two vehicles have covered areas that would normally require four.

The only questionable feature of this system is the requirement that passengers rearrange themselves while the vehicle is still moving. Of course, this is done constantly on the New York City subways, and for less reason, namely to be closer to an exit or stairway. In truth, it is only dangerous during the lurching starts and stops experienced in the antiquated subway system, and during sharp curves. In a modern system, starts and stops as well as curves could be much smoother. Actually, when the railbus is in steady motion, it is no different from any other train, in which people have been walking and even eating for many years.

Really then, the rearrangement simply amounts to a one-time round of "musical chairs" for some of the passengers; the rest will already be in the right car. In exchange for this, the passengers can enjoy rapid, practically door-to-door, transportation.

Robert F. McLean of General Motors has a suggestion that might even eliminate the musical chairs aspect, although at the cost of some small amount of time. Rather than a "rendezvous" *en route*, the buses would pull into interchanges set along major routes. Passengers would change to the proper coaches at these interchanges, after which the vehicles would continue on their way.

Naturally, the railbus systems are in the relatively distant future. The first steps may already have been taken, however. The Port of New York Authority, in cooperation with the Metropolitan Transportation Authority, has initiated a test program to determine the practicability of a bus-rail vehicle.

Such a vehicle, utilizing retractible steel wheels as well as rubber tires (see photo), could by-pass a large part of the current traffic bottleneck by making part of the run between Manhattan and Kennedy International Airport on existing Long Island Rail Road trackage. It would perform as a regular bus at both ends of the trip. Should the testing show the vehicle to be technically practicable, the feasibility of its commercial use will be further investigated. The advantage of the

A Railbus with Steel and Rubber Wheels

bus, of course, is that of all forms of public transit, it comes closest to providing door-to-door transportation.

Exciting and promising though such systems may be, we must face the fact that many people would still prefer to travel in their own cars. Others may simply not live close enough to a transit station to make that system attractive. While cars could be left under the control of individual drivers, it is more logical, for the reasons given in Chapter Five, to automate the system. With electric cars and guideways for steering, the system is a relatively simple one, or at least much simpler than that needed for gasoline-engined cars. The electric car can draw both propulsion energy and steering guidance from the guideway.

Several systems have been proposed. One, the Alden *StaRRcar* (for Self Transit Rail and Road), is shown. It utilizes its own rubber tires for suspension and propulsion, but is guided along a concrete guideway. While it can be propelled by its own electric motor, it can also be whizzed downtown on a track which would guide, control and power the car. Close headways would be computer-controlled and speeds would be around 60 mph.

At the station, one of several conveniently located in the CBD, the motorist simply gets out of the car. It is then set aside until someone else needs it; perhaps it is dispatched for use elsewhere.

At night, the driver picks up the first available car, travels along the guideway to his local stop, then drives along local streets until he reaches home. He can then keep the car overnight, in which case the charge would be higher than for the simple trip from station to station.

Another possibility, proposed by researchers at Cornell Aero-

122

Alden's StaRRcar

nautical Laboratory, is the *Urbmobile*. Although the Urbmobile is similar in concept to the StaRRcar, various suspension systems are being considered under a $100,000 study
contract. One possible form envisions the Urbmobile traveling
like a railroad car as shown, utilizing flanged steel wheels on
steel rails for travel on the guideway, and regular rubber tires
for local street travel. The steel wheels would be on the same
axles but "inside" the rubber wheels, just as in the bus-rail
vehicle shown on page 121.

Preliminary work suggests a vehicle with a top speed of
40 mph on the tires and 60 mph on the guideway. It would
have a range of at least 40 miles between each charge, which
could be accomplished in the manner described earlier for any
electric car. It would also be possible to charge the battery
while the vehicle is traveling along the guideway. Lead-acid
batteries will be investigated, along with the more advanced
batteries and fuel cells now under development (see Chapter
Six).

Estimated size of the Urbmobile will be 12 to 13 feet long
and five feet wide. Unloaded weight will be some 2,000 pounds.
(A standard Volkswagen is 12 feet long, five feet wide, and
weighs 1,764 pounds.) Small buses and freight vehicles will
also be considered.

A normal 12-foot-wide expressway lane carries an average
of 3,000 people an hour in rush hours. The small size of the
Urbmobile, the close spacing possible, and the guided mode
of travel promise movement of as many as 20,000 people per
hour along an eight-foot guideway.

In the study, researchers are laying out a system on paper
with 15 to 25 miles of automatic guideway along the most
heavily traveled routes from downtown Buffalo to suburbs

The Urbmobile

north and east of the city, with perhaps a spur to the south also. Stations will be spotted about one mile apart in the core, and two to three miles apart farther out. Terminals for automatic storage of Urbmobiles will be located at these points. There will also be parking areas for standard automobiles whose owners might want to use the Urbmobile to get to work.

As with the StaRRcar, the big advantages of the Urbmobile are reduction of air pollution, through using electricity, and of congestion, since each standard-size American car occupies more than 200 square feet of space 24 hours a day. At the same time, the motorist is afforded door-to-door mobility and convenience. Finally, the system is also thought of as a possible high-speed intercity link.

One of the goals of the study is to determine the best possible combination of guideway and vehicle, and then to com-

A Car-on-train Pallet System

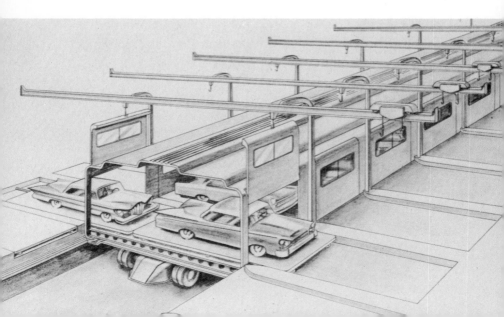

pare this with a *pallet type system*. In this, the car is driven onto a platform, or "pallet," which is then transported along the guideway. This is similar in principle to the car-on-train systems we mentioned earlier.

For example, seen here is a Westinghouse concept that provides the car-carrying equivalent of the PeopleMover. As you can see in the second drawing, the operation has been taken out of the hands of the driver once he parks his car on the pad or pallet. Now flat tires, stalled engines, and so on cannot hold up the entire operation. Since the motive power for the entire system rests in conventional, highly perfected electric induction motors, reliability of the system should be high.

We are, of course, still plagued with the problem of intermediate stops. As usual, someone has made a proposal which takes this into account. Edward N. Hall of United Aircraft proposes mile-long trains which never stop from one end of their run to the other. Pre-loaded shuttle cars accelerate from the station, lock onto the through-train, exchange palletized autos (rather as we did with passenger capsules on page 116), and then dip below the track and finally come to a stop on the other side. There, the procedure is reversed for trains which come from the opposite direction.

It should be pointed out that while the StaRRcar and Urbmobile systems appear simpler and perhaps more desirable than the pallet systems at first glance, there are even more serious technical difficulties in implementing them. Let us just suppose that a car is derailed for some reason, or simply loses power.

The long headways on expressways serve a purpose. They allow following cars to be brought to a halt before colliding with the car in trouble. On a train system, or even in a locked-convoy grouping of cars, if a problem arises the whole train simply slows down *as a unit*. People may be thrown out of their seats, it is true; but 200 cars don't go ploughing into one another.

Urbmobile planners are inclined to feel that the reliability problem is not insurmountable. For example, the cars might be built so that they all brake automatically and at the same rate when power is cut off. This could be arranged to happen automatically when something goes wrong. Thus, the spacing would remain the same as the cars rolled to a stop.

By setting up the system on a 25-foot-wide right-of-way (about the same width as two expressway lanes), two opposing lanes of Urbmobiles could flank a center service strip. In case of trouble, power could be cut off from an entire sector, and a service vehicle would speed to the trouble spot, lift out the car in trouble, and start the system up again.

This is typical of the problems and possibilities that must be evaluated and answered in the Urbmobile study. While the system is visualized for some time around 1985, it is felt that if all goes well, and if interest is high enough (which means if funding is received), an actual system could be put into operation within five to seven years—an exciting prospect.

Piggy-back, pod, pallet, or individual-vehicle/guideway— which shall it be? Most probably, *all* will find use somewhere and sometime in the future.

8

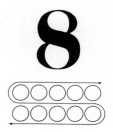

Above and Below the Sea

THE SMART, trim, 65-foot *H.S. Victoria* slips away from her pier near the heart of downtown Seattle. Carrying 75 passengers, she cruises leisurely toward the open water of Puget Sound.

Once clear of the harbor traffic, the *Victoria* leaps forward as the captain unleashes the power of two 1,000-horsepower gas turbine engines. At just over 20 mph, the rapidly accelerating craft begins climbing out of the water. A few moments later, she has reached more than 40 mph and is literally flying.

The captain sets his course directly toward his destination, right into—rather than around—the storm he is expecting. As the *Victoria* knifes into the squall, her 40-ton hull soars 8 to 10 feet above the surface of the water, well above the waves. Only rain and spray reach the craft; the leaping waves break harmlessly beneath her. Inside the comfortable cabin, the 75 passengers, well tended by pretty stewardesses, sit snug and comfortable.

Just ninety minutes after leaving Seattle, the *Victoria* ties up at her terminal in the Canadian city for which she was named. She has slashed more than three hours from the time required by a normal passenger ferry.

At first glance, the *Victoria* looks pretty much like any other passenger boat of its size. In fact, the shape of the hull is very similar to any other high-speed boat. The difference lies in the wing-like structures that project below the bottom of the boat's keel. These provide lift to the craft in exactly the same manner that wings provide lift to an aircraft. The foils, however, can be much smaller, since water is so much more dense than air. At high speed, the small foils provide enough lifting force to bring the entire craft right up and out of the water.

Since there is so much less mass traveling through the water, resistance is cut considerably and speeds can go up. There are *hydrofoils* in operation today which have speeds up to about 70 mph. Others in development will have speeds well over 100 mph. The 46-mph *Victoria* is a commercial craft, and has sacrificed some speed to passenger-carrying ability and comfort.

Submerged foils are only part of the reason why the *Victoria* can cut through rough seas without discomfort to her passengers. Each of the foils has movable control surfaces tied into an automatic flight control system similar to those used in jet aircraft. As we mentioned earlier, mechanical and electronic equipment can react much faster than man. As forces are generated by sea and wind which tend to toss the *Victoria* around, sensors detect them and "give orders" to the foils

The High-Speed Flying Ferry, Victoria

which keep the craft on an even keel. Thus, passengers can sit comfortably while the sea thrashes about beneath them.

As we know, life on the water was not always this pleasant. For thousands of years, wind and wave conspired now and then to make water journeys unbelievably miserable affairs. Only a century and a quarter ago, Charles Dickens wrote of a trip he took to America:

> What the agitation of a steam-vessel is, on a bad winter's night in the wild Atlantic, it is impossible for the most vivid imagination to conceive. To say that she is flung down on her side in the waves, with her masts dipping into them, and that, springing up again, she rolls over on the other side,

131

until a heavy sea strikes her with the noise of a hundred great guns, and hurls her back—and that she stops, and staggers, and shivers, as though stunned, and then, with a violent throbbing at her heart, darts onward like a monster goaded into madness, to be beaten down, and battered, and crushed, and leaped on by the angry sea . . . is nothing.

Waves are not only involved in making the ride a rough one now and then. They are the main reason that conventional ship design is limited to some 35 mph. Surface vessels *create* waves as well as take them. The faster the ship travels, the larger these waves; small-boat enthusiasts have shaken many a fist, at least mentally, at large, fast boats whose waves have threatened to engulf them. The energy that goes into creating these waves, as well as other, less obvious turbulence, can come from only one place: the ship's propulsion mechanism. Such

A 70-mph Hydrofoil

energy is simply subtracted from the energy that can be put into propulsion.

Not only do hydrofoils provide a smooth ride, then, but they also break the conventional speed barrier by keeping the hull out of the water (thus reducing drag as well as wave-making), and by having only the knife-like struts and the foils cutting through the water. Hydrofoil craft have already been put into service in a number of areas all over the world.

While hydrofoil craft are useful along rivers and on coastal runs, it is unlikely that they will be used for transportation purposes along deep-sea routes, even with more development. Research has indicated that the largest practical displacement for hydrofoil craft ranges somewhere between 500 to 2,000 tons.

This is quite small by current ocean-going standards. The giant *Queen Mary*, now retired from service, weighed about 80,000 tons. More typical ocean liners range in the 20,000-30,000 ton class.

In hydrofoils, the larger the ship, the larger the fins needed to lift it. But the weight of the fin increases at a faster rate than its lifting power, which means that efficiency goes down as size goes up.

There is another, and newer, kind of vessel where this is not so. The *surface effect ship* (*SES*)—a variation of the air-supported trains we have already discussed—becomes *more* efficient as the size increases. That is, it takes less power per pound to drive a 10,000 SES than it does a 5,000 tonner. Both military and civilian planners, eager to shatter the speed limits imposed by conventional large-ship design, see some rather fantastic things in store.

One possibility is a 5,000 or 10,000 ton ship crossing the

North Atlantic in thirty-five hours, well under half of today's record. Shippers, now faced with a choice of either fast delivery at a high price (i.e., aircraft), or low speed at a low price (freighters), would welcome such a development. Such ships could even provide truly inexpensive ocean travel for passengers. However, as we shall see, the airlines are mounting some stiff competition, even in this area, with their giant jets.

Just as the hydrofoil flies, so does the SES, but in a different manner. The name, "surface effect ship," is derived from the fact that it operates above the surface of the water, supported solely on a cushion of air.

There are two major ways of supplying this cushion. One is aerodynamically, wherein air moving by at high speeds acts on airfoil surfaces to provide lift. Two designs are possible. In the Weiland airfoil type, actual wing-like structures are used. In the channel-flow type, the underside of the craft itself acts as the airfoil.

For various technical reasons, the aerodynamic type has been more or less bypassed (so far) in favor of the second major type, the aerostatic lift vehicle. This type is also called the *air cushion vehicle, or ACV* (see Chapter Three). Here the craft forces enough air down through its bottom surface to maintain a cushion of air between it and the surface below.

As with the air-cushion train discussed earlier, pressure must be maintained under the craft by the continuous addition of new air to replace that which leaks out from the back, front, and sides of the craft. Typically, the SES is also propelled forward by the use of separate aircraft-type propellers, although other methods of propulsion are under consideration. A speed of 150 mph is considered well within the realm of the SES.

134

One way to increase the over-all efficiency of this type of craft is to surround the air with some form of enclosure, in order to cut down on leakage. The result is a "captured air bubble." For example, Booz, Allen Applied Research, Inc., designed a vessel of this type for the U.S. Department of Commerce. In this craft, projected at about 1,000 tons, the sides are dropped into the water. At the same time, a flexible set of "skis" rides the water at front and rear, to adjust for the rise and fall of the sea as the craft speeds along. Design data have also been provided by Booz, Allen for vessels up to 10,000 tons.

While ships of this size and design remain projections for the future, a number of smaller ACV's have been built and are now in service. Both the Russians and the British possess extensive coastal waters and have done considerable work along these lines. The Russians are testing a 50-passenger, 75-mph craft on the Volga River.

For their part, the English are represented by the world's largest ACV, the 165-ton SRN-4. Shown on page 139, the vessel can shuttle some 600 passengers across the English Channel in thirty-five minutes at speeds of 70 to 75 mph. Alternatively, the SRN-4 can carry about 30 autos and 100 to 200 people.

In America, the Bell Aerosystems Company has gone into production with a family of ACVs at its main plant near Buffalo, N.Y. Among them are a 39-foot, 7-tonner capable of carrying 15 persons or a 7,000 pound payload; a 48½-foot, 10-tonner which can carry 33 persons or 10,000 pounds; and a 56-foot, 25-tonner which can carry 90 persons or 24,000 pounds. This last has twin 1,150-hp turbine engines driving two three-bladed, nine-foot props and two seven-foot lift fans.

135

Two of the 39-footers, designated SK-5's or Jet Skimmers, have been used in a highly successful demonstration passenger service across San Francisco Bay.

While none of these craft is of ocean-going capability, all of them offer something very special in return: namely, the capability of riding over the surface of the water without touching it. They can travel across ice and debris and even up onto land, with no trouble at all.

Think of what this would mean to inhabitants of such places as Pelee Island, in Ontario, Canada. Here, residents are quite isolated from both the Canadian and American mainlands after the winter ice has formed on Lake Erie. The township's council recently passed a resolution urging the Province of Ontario to consider establishing ACV service between the island and the mainland.

Due to the nature of the vessels, ACVs are often called *"hovercraft."* Since they are not limited to water, they are sometimes also called *"gems,"* or *ground effect machines.*

Military men are, of course, also intrigued with the possibilities of such versatile craft. They can see (and are experimenting with) smaller gems zipping along at 70 mph, then sailing right onto land at somewhat lower speeds to deliver combat troops and supplies to points several miles inland. Commercial shippers may be able to find widespread use for such craft, since they can eliminate a double transfer (from land to water and then back again).

Large-scale development along these lines could even cause important changes in economic and political situations. Coastal cities, now extremely important because of their proximity to water (though no longer as important as they were before the

137

development of railroads, trucks, and aircraft), might see a further decline in relative importance.

However, it is unlikely that coastal cities such as Boston, New York, and San Francisco will be deserted in the next few years. ACVs are certainly not the complete answer to all the problems besetting shippers and travelers; no one service can be. Indeed, a number of serious problems remain to be licked.

Unless the hovercraft is operating in virtual wilderness, travel at high speed in fog or darkness can be extremely hazardous. In and around coastal waters and on rivers, however, travel at high speed is dangerous even under *good* conditions. Boats, in general, are less maneuverable than landcraft, especially at higher speeds; without contact with solid matter, they tend to skid during turns. Obviously, hovercraft are even more subject to this problem.

This is one of the reasons I have chosen to discuss gems in the chapter on watercraft. They could, obviously, be grouped with landcraft as well. We have all read or heard of the car of the future which will be supported by pads or cushions of air. This sounds fine, but unless exclusive rights-of-way are provided, I would hate to be around when the first one tries to maneuver in traffic.

For those who might be interested, let me repeat Newton's second law of motion: *A body in motion tends to remain in motion, and will continue moving in the same direction, unless acted upon by some external force.* In cars, that force is the friction of tire on pavement—for both stopping and turning. In the typical ship, the force is a combination of water resistance, water against rudder, and perhaps reversal of propellers. The same techniques can be used for air but are far less effective.

World's Largest Hovercraft

Thus it is that the only landcraft seriously being considered along these directions are the air-supported trains we have already discussed.

Hydrofoils are not plagued with this problem. Indeed, the vertical surfaces make them very maneuverable and reduce the tendency all boats have to side-slip during turns. But hydrofoils have other problems. One is that they require relatively deep channels when they are not "flying." Many are built with retractable foils to get around this problem.

Another difficulty is that of debris in the water. At the slow speeds of conventional marine vessels, logs and other floating hazards are likely to be simply pushed aside by the solid hull. The combination of high speeds and slim supporting struts could make floating debris a real problem to hydrofoils. Ex-

139

perience at the speeds so far attained, however, show that the smaller objects most often encountered are actually pushed aside or even broken up by the strongly built struts. In the unusual case of a large, hard object, the craft are designed so that, upon impact, the foils will break off without ripping a hole in the hull, and the vessel simply settles into the water. However, rapid deceleration would result, with possible injury to passengers.

But we have heard objections like these before, and they have invariably been satisfactorily handled. John Jones, assistant to the President of North American Aviation, envisions gas turbine propelled, hydrofoil merchant ships capable of speeds up to 300 mph.

Commercial Submarines

While man has used the water for transportation purposes for thousands of years, during virtually all that time he has been effectively glued to its surface. Half a century ago, he began flying over its waves. Even here, in the air, lightning, ice, hail, fog, and wind can be dangerous foes. Now, more and more, mariners are considering the approach taken by Jules Verne's fictional Captain Nemo, who, in his palacial submarine *Nautilus,* traveled at up to 50 mph in perfect comfort no matter how violent the environment above him. And Verne's *20,000 Leagues Under the Sea* was written all the way back in 1870!

The development of nuclear-powered ships, such as the American and West German merchant vessels *Savannah* and *Otto Hahn,* and the Russian icebreaker *Lenin,* as well as the experience gained in our nuclear submarines and in rapidly widening undersea exploration, may all point the way to use of the submarine for commercial shipping and travel. If this still seems unlikely to you, consider the following factors.

Commercial submarines traveling Arctic sea routes would greatly reduce the trading and traveling distances of the world. The present route from Tokyo to London is 12,800 miles; by polar passage (under the ice), it shrinks to 7,500 miles. Similarly, a ship traveling from Seattle to Oslo, Norway, via the Panama Canal, covers 10,700 miles; via the Arctic shortcut, the trip would only be 7,000 miles.

Then, of course, there is the advantage of not having to cope with the vagaries of the weather. If any of you have been through or even in the vicinity of a hurricane, you will appreciate being able to stay out of its way. I can recall being on the *Queen Mary,* one of the largest ships ever afloat, in the general area of a hurricane. Even that giant vessel was rolling and pitching to a considerable degree.

I can clearly remember watching my bathrobe, hanging on a hook behind the door of my stateroom, appear to swing out from the wall by 20 degrees or so, as the ship rolled away from it. Ropes had to be strung across all the decks to ensure safe passage across them, for in addition to sharp pitching and rolling, we had to contend with 60 to 80 mph winds. I can also remember the almost-empty dining room; most of the passengers had lost all desire to eat.

But the clearest image I have is that of an obviously seasoned traveler who was comfortably seated on a deck chair, wrapped in a blanket, and smoking a pipe. I admired his calm demeanor. Now, keep in mind the fact that this was taking place on the top deck, some 85 feet above the waterline. Sud-

denly, even as I watched, a giant wave broke over the deck, completely drenching the man, Fortunately, the wave had no strength at this height and he was not washed overboard. He sat there for a moment, tapped out his pipe, shrugged his shoulders, and went below.

An 85-foot wave! Clearly, even a surface-effect ship which travels ten feet above the water will have trouble managing a sea like that. The cruise ship *Queen of Bermuda* took a considerable beating during the same storm. One crewman was killed and a number of passengers were injured.

Another advantage of the submarine is that it doesn't *make* waves. This alone may make it possible for undersea craft to get up to very high speeds. Nuclear submarines already can maintain steady speeds of more than 30 mph (their actual speed is considered classified information by the government). The Navy is interested in hydrofoils and ACVs, since conventional surface craft have trouble keeping up with the fast subs.

Various kinds of research point toward underwater speeds of 100 mph and up. For example, it has long been known that the dolphin is able to move through water at top speed, hour after hour with minimum effort. Even though subs don't make waves, they still create turbulence as they move through the water. The dolphins seem to have a complex body system which overcomes this and which permits what is called *laminar flow* along their bodies.

Part of the explanation lies in the animal's streamlined body contours. But his loose, rubber-like outer skin also has been found to play an important part in the process. There is even evidence that the dolphin employs a complex, brain-controlled system that provides laminar flow under various conditions by compensating for variations in pressure, density, temperature, and saltiness of the water, and even for current and the slow waves that sometimes occur below the surface.

In another attack on the problem of underwater speed, North American Aviation engineers are experimenting with various shapes which may be used in later craft. Speeds of 115 mph have already been achieved. One engineer has speculated on attaining speeds up to that of sound in water, or about 3,400 mph! David E. McNay, project engineer at North American, says this is something like attaining orbital speed in the atmosphere.

While this seems an unlikely possibility, new developments in light and high-strength materials may make super-stream-

143

lining easier. (The strongest shape is inherently a sphere, which is clearly not a good shape for high-speed travel.) New developments in power generation, such as a thermonuclear fusion engine (a major step beyond even the current nuclear fission reactors), could supply the necessary power.

Still other technical difficulties exist which must be overcome. Since light does not travel far in water, travel at high speeds will require other means of "seeing." New developments in the exciting field of three-dimensional laser photography, or *holography*, may point the way. *Sonar* (sound navigation and ranging), which is now used, can tell us that something is in front of us, but not what it is. Douglas Aircraft engineers are investigating the potential of *acoustical holography*. Sound, after all, is a wave motion, just as light is; it may be possible to "see by sound," which travels better through the water than light does.

Navigation is another obstacle that is being surmounted with the aid of modern technology. Already in operation are devices which can navigate both air and sea craft with no reference whatever to the outside world. The method is called *inertial navigation* and is used on most of our large rockets and military aircraft, and on all our nuclear subs. The submarine *Nautilus*, which passed under the ice of the North Pole in 1958, was guided largely in this way.

Athelstan Spilhaus, dean of the University of Minnesota's Institute of Technology, points out:

"Although submarines have thus far been used principally for military purposes, the advantages of traveling below the disturbed interface between ocean and atmosphere with its waves, windstorms, and ice mean that submarine freight and passenger travel, as well as a variety of submarine vessels for research purposes, will undoubtedly be developed."

Any of the developments we have spoken of can help to make this prediction a reality, as can another one which some researchers have been considering for several years: a sub that can fly! A study has already been carried out by General Dynamics/Convair for the Bureau of Naval Weapons. Emphasis was placed on a moderate flying range of 300 to 500 miles, along with an underwater range of 50 miles at 6 mph and 75-foot depth capability. Engineers said the craft, which the Navy called the *Subplane*, would weigh eight tons and would have a 500 to 1,500 pound payload. It would fly at 175 to 250 mph and would have a retractable ski to assist in take-off.

While a missile has been developed that can do everything mentioned above and more, much work remains to be done before we see a *manned* flying sub. In the meantime, we might note that Japanese government and industry people have already collaborated on the design of a nuclear merchant submarine; it is now being studied for commercial feasibility. Large air-cushion and hydrofoil ships powered by nuclear reactors have also been proposed and have high potential for development.

9

Aircraft—
Up and Away

In the year 1892, William Harben published a science-fiction
story called "In the Year Ten Thousand."* He described our
descendants, a race of beings which had evolved far beyond
us—in intellect, in beauty, and in gentleness. He also had
something to say about air travel. Remember that what you
read now was written in 1892, eleven years before the Wright
Brothers' flight:

> The old man and his son left the museum [where they
> were looking over such old-fashioned things as books, maga-
> zines, and pictures of our ugly faces] and walked into a
> wonderful park. Flowers of the most beautiful kinds and of
> sweetest fragrance grew on all sides. They came to a tall

* Reprinted in *Future Perfect, American Science Fiction of the Nineteenth Century*, by H. Bruce Franklin, Oxford University Press, N.Y., 1966.

tower, four thousand feet in height, built of manufactured crystal. Something, like a great white bird, a thousand feet long, flew across the sky and settled down on the tower's summit.

"This was one of the most wonderful inventions of the Seventieth Century," said the old man. "The early inhabitants of the earth could not have dreamed that it would be possible to go around it in twenty-four hours. In fact, there was a time when they were not able to go around it at all. Scientists were astonished when a man called Malburn, a great inventor, announced that, at a height of four thousand feet, he could disconnect an air ship from the laws of gravitation, and cause it to stand still in space till the earth had turned over."

In 1892, the farthest stretch of Harben's imagination saw 1,000 mph as the ultimate in speed. Yet today, more than eight thousand years before the 100th century, rockets attain speeds of 25,000 mph on flights to the moon and other planets; the manned rocket plane X-15 has exceeded 4,000 mph on short flights through the atmosphere; and operational military aircraft regularly fly at 2,000 mph. If it is really necessary, a man can easily get from New York to San Francisco in an hour and a half.

As we know, however, it still takes longer than that for the rest of us to get from New York to Boston or from San Francisco to Los Angeles. We have discussed one possible answer: high-speed ground transportation. But there are limitations to this approach; the high cost of guideway equipment and right-of-way limit its use to densely populated areas. Even a transcontinental tube-train would only have stops or branch-offs at the larger cities.

If we are to prevent our country from turning into a few

gargantuan metropolitan areas, we must make the medium and small cities more accessible to one another and to the larger cities as well. Aircraft are marvelously flexible in that they need ground equipment, i.e., airports, only at the ends of the flight. However, with the rapid increases that have been taking place in flying, airports have been getting more and more crowded.

And with larger craft doing the flying, airports are becoming larger and larger. Kennedy International Airport, serving Metropolitan New York, covers 7½ square miles, an area equal to all of Manhattan Island south of 42nd Street. You don't put an airport like that in, or even very close to, a large city. (Kennedy Airport is fifteen highway miles from the city, Newark Airport is thirteen, and LaGuardia is seven.) A fourth jetport is needed in the New York area, but large tracts of available land are becoming increasingly scarce. One favored area is seventy miles away from Manhattan.

Helicopters and VTOLs

While helicopters are ideal for getting into and out of small areas vertically, they are slow in horizontal flight. Conventional aircraft are fine for covering horizontal distances swiftly, but they need large landing areas. What aviation has been seeking right along, and is still seeking, is aircraft that combine the most desirable features of the two.

Actually, the helicopter has come a long way in this time. Although normal cruising speed is only about 80 to 100 mph, for certain jobs, where hovering for relatively long periods is required, it is unsurpassed. For such operations as rescue,

148

construction, fire fighting, and surveillance (wartime or traffic), it has proved itself many times over. One helicopter, the Hughes HeavyLifter, can haul twice its own weight.

However, not only is the "chopper" slow, but it is expensive, both to buy and to maintain. The main problem is the large rotor which causes severe vibration problems. New York Airways reports that 20 man-hours of maintenance are required for every hour in the air.

Helicopters are also useful for, and are used for, short passenger trips, as from the Wall Street Heliport in lower Manhattan to the major airports in the surrounding areas. But because of high costs, they haven't yet been able to pay their own way. Some of the airlines have recently begun subsidizing helicopter service (after government aid ran out), since it makes air flight more attractive for those who are in a real hurry—and willing to pay for the fast service.

The 45 to 60 minute bus ride from the east side of Manhattan to Kennedy International Airport costs $2. The helicopter flight from the Wall Street Heliport runs $10, but takes only 12 to 14 minutes.

In 1966, New York Airways carried 190,000 passengers between two Manhattan terminals (the Pan Am Building and the Wall Street Heliport in lower Manhattan) and the three major airports. This was only a small fraction of the city's more than 28 million air travelers. (One of every four domestic flights in the entire United States begins or ends in the New York area.) New York Airways is counting on increased acceptance for the service, and increasing congestion on the ground, to provide even greater patronage in the coming years.

Naturally, prices could come down if more people use the

service. On the other hand, one can never be sure that more widely available service would result in the kind of patronage that would be required to support it. But planners are inclined to feel that this would occur.

A project now being studied could tell the story: a monumental structure which would serve as a transportation terminal, with heliport facilities. The idea is similar in principle to the Cornell Aeronautical Laboratory concept, the *Master Mode-mixer*, shown on the next two pages.

To be located on the East River, which runs along the east side of Manhattan, the eight-storied building would cover two large city blocks and a bit of the river. Tentative plans provide parking space for up to 2,000 cars, facilities for baggage and cargo-handling airline offices, taxi and bus ramps, and connections on the river for hydrofoil craft. Since part of the building would extend out over the river, most of the helicopter departures and approaches could be made over water, thus minimizing a current problem of noise in the CBD.

The large, flat roof would be able to handle a number of the 70-plus passenger 'copters now being planned and built. These will be much more economical to run than today's smaller models. The cost of flying seventy passengers in one craft is obviously far less than for seven passengers in each of ten different craft. With improvements in instrument flying, which would provide reliable flights even in poor weather, the new service should attract new passengers.

If other cities should follow suit, there is the even more attractive prospect of direct flights, at 180 mph or faster, between city centers several hundred miles apart throughout the country.

For the super-cities of the future, this may be a way of reducing airport, as well as road, congestion. Cities such as Washington, Baltimore, Boston, and Philadelphia account for almost 30 per cent of all domestic passenger traffic in the New York airports. If CBD-to-CBD vertical take-off and landing (VTOL) service is instituted in these cities, a substantial share of the load on the airports and on the airport roads could be eliminated. Out of 54 million air passengers in 1964, more than half flew trips of less than five hundred miles.

Los Angeles Airways is contemplating an intriguing plan which is reminiscent of the road-rail systems we discussed in Chapter Seven. In the *Skybus* program, a large Sikorsky Flying Crane would carry a detachable passenger pod. At either end of the flight, the pod could operate as a bus—either self-propelled or drawn by a tractor—with all the advantages that normal bus travel offers. In effect, we have a VTOL bus.

Another term you may have seen is STOL, which stands for *short* take-off and landing. Since this is generally nothing more than a compromise between a normal aircraft and a VTOL, we shall concentrate on the latter, even though STOLs are in truth more economical. Furthermore, virtually all the craft we shall describe shortly can also operate in the STOL mode where more landing space is available. Thus, you may see many of them designated V/STOL.

All VTOLs pose difficult technical problems. While an ordinary aircraft can develop lift slowly by increasing speed along a runway, the VTOL must take off without this kind of help. It seeks all its initial lift without any forward speed. This requires a great amount of lifting power, which is likely to be needed only for take-off and landing. The result is lower payload, higher costs, and shorter range. Typical range for a helicopter is only a few hundred miles.

151

The Master Mode-Mixer: An All-Transport Terminal

Operating costs are improving, but are still ten or fifteen times higher than those of conventional aircraft. Nevertheless, for reasons given earlier, there is no question that there is a place for VTOLs. Many feel that the medium-range market, in the 100 to 500 mile region, is where the VTOL will make its greatest mark—assuming a satisfactory design can be found.

One of the reasons for the slowness of the typical chopper is the fact that the large rotor is used for both horizontal and vertical flight. In some models, the craft simply "leans" forward for horizontal flight, thus transferring some of the thrust from the vertical to the horizontal direction. In others, the more complicated approach of varying the pitch of the blades as they sweep around is used. Although pure helicopters have gotten up to well over 200 mph, very high power is required. These craft, therefore, are very inefficient at high speed.

Unlike standard aircraft, larger engines and streamlining are not the answer. The critical factor is the rotor. In addition to aerodynamic problems in high-speed rotation, the rotor is large and can only take so much speed of rotation before it tears itself to pieces.

The development and substitution of turbine engines for conventional piston engines has been useful, however. (We mentioned this type of engine earlier, in connection with the New York-Boston TurboTrain.) The weight of a helicopter turbine engine is less than half that of a piston engine producing the same horsepower. Hence, the craft can carry a greater payload; or it can carry two engines, either of which provides enough power to support it. Thus, there is a built-in safety factor.

Since the rotor can't be speeded up past a certain point,

A Compound Helicopter

other approaches to higher speeds are necessary. For example, the power of the rotor can be augmented by the addition of a separate means of driving the craft in forward motion. The result is a hybrid, or compound, helicopter. The rotor of a compound craft is powered as usual for take-off; when the desired altitude is reached, power is transferred to a conventional propeller or jet for forward thrust. At this point, the rotor is allowed to freewheel, that is, spin freely, as the craft moves through the air. This provides some lift, but not enough. Stubby wings are used for additional lift.

While the compound is an advance (speeds of well over 275 mph have been reached), it is not an ideal solution. The freewheeling rotor is more hindrance than aid; and the wings, stubby though they may be, interfere with the downwash action of the main rotor in vertical flight. The additional weight of the wings and drive units also detracts from payload.

A number of different kinds of VTOL have been built (see photos) or are under study. An obvious possibility is to tilt the rotor or rotors forward, once the desired altitude has been achieved in vertical flight. While this is not practicable with the usual single large rotor, or even the tandem design (one behind the other), a pair of rotors at the wing tips has been tried with good success.

A basic design is that of the Bell *Tilt-Rotor*. This particular design, which has not yet been built, is based on flight experience with an earlier machine which achieved conversion in flight in 1958.

Another possibility is to stop the rotor, fold it, and perhaps stow it away during cruise flight. Such a design promises greatly improved speed. However, the system would be complicated and probably heavy. Also, wind-tunnel tests have shown that the rotor is tricky to stop and start in forward flight. When the blade slows down below freewheeling speed, it loses the rigidity imparted by its spin and starts flopping around, sometimes quite violently.

A possible way out is to redesign the rotor(s) and to make them part of the aircraft's fixed wing structure during forward flight. Hughes Tool Company engineers maintain that a potential speed of 500 mph is possible with such a configuration.

For the stowed-rotor design, assuming good streamlining can be achieved, there appears to be no practical limit on speed. Some feel, however, that sufficient rotor strength with practical weight for the conversion process can't be achieved

World's Largest VTOL: The X-142A

Bell Aerosystems' X-22A

with today's materials. Super-strength materials, now in development, could be the answer here.

One example, which consists of tiny, thread-like boron filiments embedded in an epoxy plastic base, provides light weight, high stiffness, and good corrosion resistance. Used until now only as a test material on the F-111 jet fighter, it has been approved for its first commercial application: replacement of an existing part on the leading wing edge of a Lockheed 200— the commercial version of the well-known Air Force C-141 Starlifter.

Boron fibers are more than twice as stiff as steel, yet are less than a third as dense. When they are put into a plastic or metal matrix (surrounding material), they form a composite with a

Tomorrow's ADAM II

stiffness per unit weight that is much higher than that of steel. The fibers are also very strong. A 190-mile length of boron fiber could support itself without breaking; the strength of steel is thus also exceeded on a weight-for-weight basis. Clearly, such a strong material will be very useful in high speed helicopter rotors, whether stowed or not.

Ling-Temco-Vought, whose entry into the experimental VTOL field is probably the furthest along, has provided us with the X-142A—the largest VTOL in the world (page 157). The commercial version, when and if built, would be called the *Downtowner*. In this design, four smaller rotors are used, and, wings as well as rotors tilt. While it appears cumbersome, the aerodynamic features of this design appear to be very satisfactory. The present aircraft already has the capability of carrying forty-four passengers at cruising speeds of more than 300 mph.

In a rather different approach from the Downtowner, the Bell Aerosystems X-22A (also shown on page 157) uses smaller rotors enclosed in ducts. Company engineers maintain that the ducted units increase the thrust of the props during take-off and landing, and serve as lifting surfaces during forward flight. With one eye on safety, they have designed the craft to be able to maintain vertical flight with one engine out. As in the X-142A, the craft can cruise in horizontal flight with any two engines turning all four props, through a system of gears and clutches (all of which add weight and complexity).

Top speed of this craft is about 325 mph, but the Bell people believe that a speed of 450 mph and even higher is a possibility. (Maximum speed of the X-142A is 430 mph.) We have already mentioned Hughes' prediction of 500 mph for its stopped-rotor design. But why stop here?

159

Another type of VTOL is called the *fan-in-wing*. The XV-5A, for example, has a five-foot-diameter fan embedded in each stubby wing. For vertical lift, valves close the jet engine tail pipes used in horizontal flight. The gases are diverted to the fan blades in the wing, causing them to spin and generate lift. This increases the thrust of the gases at the expense of speed, which, of course, is not needed for landing or take-off anyway. Thus, relatively small quantities of high-speed gases are converted by the fans into large quantities of lower energy, high-mass air flow. Maximum speed has already been demonstrated to be 547 mph, and range is about 1,000 miles.

All the craft we have discussed so far have had vertical lift capability "tacked" on to conventional airframes (or vice versa, if you prefer). The future may see even more novel designs.

A model of the strange-looking ADAM II has already been built and is being tested (page 158). ADAM stands for *Air Deflection and Modulation*. Turbofan engines will be located right in the wings and nose, as shown. To obtain upward thrust, the fixed-wing design diverts air flow downward through a series of louvers or slats. ADAM is planned as a high-subsonic craft, which may bring it into the 600 mph class.

Finally, as if you didn't expect it, work is proceeding on several supersonic, jet-driven VTOLs. These, as well as the XV-5A and ADAM, are the kind of high-performance aircraft that must sacrifice payload and economy of operation to obtain this high performance. Therefore, for the time being at least, they are of more interest to the military than to commercial operators.

Jumbo Jets

As has happened so often in the past, however, what the military does today is put into commercial use tomorrow. A good example is that of the jumbo, or giant, jets. Originally conceived as a giant military transport or cargo plane (the Lockheed C-5A), these football-field–size craft begin to rival the thousand-foot airship mentioned by William Farben, and may revolutionize the air transportation business. They promise to double, triple, or even quadruple the capacity of the largest of today's jets, which are pretty big right now. The L-500, commercial version of the C-5A, will be able to carry 850 passengers, although it is more likely that a good part of the capacity will go to cargo at first.

The Lockheed 500: An Aerial Cargo Giant

So gigantic is the craft that shaving one-thousandth of an inch off the thickness of the paint will save 2,000 pounds of weight. Length is 246 feet, wingspread 222 feet, and the tail is 65 feet high—roughly five stories tall.

There will, of course, be problems at first. Running 500 passengers through customs, or even handling the vast amount of baggage involved, will provide a giant-size headache. So will making sure that runways are strong enough to take the great weights involved. Part of this problem will be solved by using many more wheels and spreading them over a wider area.

On the brighter side, there will be fewer of these giant birds landing and taking off, and fewer in the air at any one time

162

for ground controllers to worry about. In addition, the same economic factors hold which we discussed for the larger helicopters.

The typical jet is already an efficient aircraft. When this efficiency is combined with the fantastic carrying capacity of the super-jets, prices for air transportation should drop considerably. For the first time, air cargo rates for medium (500 to 1,500 miles) and long hauls will come within striking distance of trucking rates. Perhaps the $50 trans-Atlantic passenger fare, which has been talked about for many years, will finally arrive. Current estimates indicate fares some 40 or 50 per cent below present rates.

This will undoubtedly accelerate the swing from ocean to air travel that has been taking place all along. Today, 86 per cent of all people who travel overseas fly, as compared to 68 per cent ten years ago.

One of the largest steamship companies, Cunard, has in the last few years retired the two largest liners in the world, the *Queen Mary* and the *Queen Elizabeth,* plus three smaller ones, because of rising costs and falling patronage. However, no one expects ocean travel to disappear entirely, and Cunard is building a new luxury liner, the *Queen Elizabeth II,* which will be smaller and more efficient than the old one.

The first of the commercial jumbo jets to go into service is the Boeing 747. It has a capacity of 350 to 490 passengers (depending on the seating arrangement), and is slightly faster than the standard jet liner. The big change, however, is in passenger comfort, made possible by the generous proportions of the plane. The size of the cabin, 190 feet long by 20 feet wide, is about twice as long and half again as wide as the cabin of the Boeing 707. While there are many more seats, they are

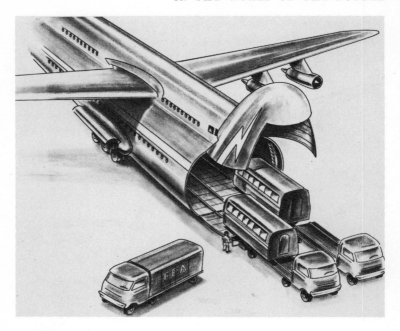

Ford's Futuristic Air Bus

wider and more generously spaced. The 747s, which should be in service by 1969 or 1970, cost $22 million apiece.

The great size and payload capacity of these giant planes will probably lead to some unusual applications, as, for example, the Ford Motor Company's idea for an *Air Bus*. Computer-dispatched buses would pick up air passengers near their homes or offices and would transfer them directly into aircraft at the airports. The process would be reversed at the landing points. This would cut down on ground congestion and parking problems; it would also eliminate the long walks to and from parking lots and other delays typically encountered in the ground/air transfer process.

164

It is on giant craft like these, too, that the first application of *nuclear propulsion* for aircraft will be seen. At ranges above 5,000 miles, a large nuclear-powered aircraft can carry a larger payload than a chemically powered airplane of the same take-off weight.

However, many technical problems remain to be solved before we see the advent of such craft. Among them is the need to include energy-absorbing structures that would enable the nuclear reactors to withstand possible crash impacts, without releasing deadly radiation.

Faster Than Sound

We probably won't see such craft for ten or more years. What we will see, however, is another kind of super-jet, the fabulous *supersonic transport*, or SST.

Just as the introduction of jet service revolutionized business and pleasure travel habits, changed world markets, and had a strong effect on international relations by "shrinking" the earth, so, too, will the SST have a great impact. With three times the speed and twice the capacity of today's jets, it will do for the Pacific what the subsonic jets did for the Atlantic: it will shrink the time between countries and tie the Far East more closely into world affairs.

In the Western Hemisphere, this craft will bring South America as close to the United States, and Africa as close to Europe, as the earlier jets brought Europe and America. New York to Buenos Aires becomes a five-hour trip—less than it takes to Paris today—rather than a bone-wearying eleven.

The development and production of such a machine will do

The Supersonic Transport, or SST

something else. It will reinforce the supremacy in aerospace capability that has made American planes the mainstay of every airline in the free world. This position has been challenged by the British-French entry into the SST sweepstakes, the Concorde, scheduled for service about 1971.

The SST, with more than twice the passenger space of the Concorde and 330 mph faster, will be the most productive long-range vehicle in history when it begins commercial operation in early 1972. Although the price tag is $36 million, as opposed to the Concorde's $18 million, the 318-footer will carry more passengers to and from Europe in a year than six *Queen Marys.*

Unfortunately, a craft which travels faster than the speed of sound through the atmosphere generates a shock wave which drags along behind it and produces what is known as the *sonic boom*. While in no way dangerous to a person in good health, the loud crack may turn out to be harmful to nervous and ill people, and simply unacceptable to others. This may preclude the use of the craft in its supersonic (faster than sound) mode over populated areas. Due to an ingenious method of changing the angle of the wings, however, the craft would be able to operate efficiently in the subsonic (below the speed of sound) mode as well. Although it is still possible that Boeing may decide on a fixed wing design, a sweep wing design is strongly favored.

With wings fully spread, control and handling at low speeds will be better than even today's subsonic jets, with their partially swept-back wings. For high-speed flight, the wings will be swung fully back, providing good aerodynamic characteristics for 1,800-mph cruising at high altitudes. Thus, the plane obtains the best of two quite different worlds—but at the cost of added weight and complexity.

The great engines of the SST (see photo) and the sweep wing will permit it to take off fully loaded at about the same speed and in less runway than a fully loaded Boeing 707. During subsonic flight, the wings will be swept to the intermediate position. For supersonic flight, the wings, hinged on giant pivot bearings, will move back to 72 degrees, producing the sleek silhouette we have seen.

Because of the sonic-boom problem, a flight from Chicago to Paris might operate like this: From Chicago to the east coast, the SST would operate subsonically, with wings in the intermediate position. As the craft heads out over the Atlantic, the wings will glide smoothly back into the sleek delta position shown and the craft will accelerate to almost three times the speed of sound. Near the end of the trip, as the coast of Europe is approached, the process will be reversed.

Should supersonic flight over land be restricted in this way, we shall once again see the ironic situation in which New York is "closer" to London than to Los Angeles (three hours vs. five), just as it was before the transcontinental railroad was built.

Professor René Miller, of the Massachusetts Institute of Technology, believes that transatlantic travel will become so commonplace that the large airlines will be operating on a no-reservation basis. They now do between New York and Washington.

Because of the high speeds involved, the usual aluminum plane skin cannot be applied; it weakens at the high temperatures that will result from air friction. The covering, parts of which will be subjected to temperatures of 2,000°F, will be constructed of the metal called titanium. Although harder to work and considerably more expensive than aluminum, it will be able to take the high temperatures, and is light in the bargain. Later models may see completely new materials take over.

Development of new materials may well become an absolute requirement. The belief held by aeronautical engineers and airline planners—namely, that whenever speed is offered people will take it—has led to plans for craft even faster than the SST. The next step is the HST, the *hypersonic transport*. And a dazzling concept it is, for we are now talking of speeds of 4,000 and 5,000 mph through the upper atmosphere!

The fastest flights so far have been made by the X-15, men-

The Hypersonic Transport, or HST

tioned at the beginning of this chapter. On November 18, 1966, the X-15-2 hit 4,250 mph, a new record for manned atmospheric flight. But the X-15 is a rocket craft and carries fuel for only a few short minutes of powered flight. For short experimental flights, this is fine; for longer trips and higher payloads within the atmosphere, other forms of propulsion, such as the ramjet, are necessary.

The ramjet lies somewhere between the jet and the rocket.

SST Engine

The next step, supersonic combustion ramjets, or *scramjets*, may even play a role in sending payloads into space. (This aspect of transportation will be covered in a subsequent book in this series.)

Someday in the future, even the X-15 may seem like the prop-driven plane seems to us now—slow and a bit old-fashioned. Plans are already on the drawing board for aircraft capable of a speed of 11,000 mph.

And why not? Materials technology is advancing rapidly and may well provide substances able to stand up against the multi-thousand degree temperatures that will be encountered.

Programs are already under way to develop a hypersonic test engine and to develop and test lightweight structures capable of operating at high speeds.

While all of this sounds rather far away at the moment, there is no theoretical reason why these or even higher speeds cannot be attained. Some aircraft experts predict we will see such craft in service by 1985 or 1990.

At 18,000 mph, however, the craft has reached orbital speed. And at 25,000 mph, the problem is no longer how to keep it up, but how to keep it *down*—that is, how to keep it from flying off into space.

Even at 11,000 mph—which can probably be attained without any revolutionary development, such as a tunnel through the earth—no two cities on earth would be more than three-quarters of an hour apart. How small would our world be then?

Epilogue

LAST TRUCK GRINDS TO HALT IN NORTHEAST CORRIDOR
ALL ROADS CLOGGED   SOME SUPPLIES ALREADY SHORT
EFFORTS TO CLEAR ROADS AND HIGHWAYS FAIL
MILLIONS OF CARS AND TRUCKS STRANDED
PRESIDENT DECLARES NATIONAL EMERGENCY,
TO SPEAK TONIGHT

THIS MIGHT BE the headline in your newspaper ten or twenty years from now. Don't think for a moment that it can't happen. On December 30, 1963, traffic in the heart of Boston did grind to a halt—and it stayed that way for more than five hours. Another severe tie-up occurred in 1967.

It is important to realize that one of the major objectives of looking into the future is to foresee the bad as well as the good. The point is that *both* are possible. For there is not *a* future—settled, solid, inexorable. There are many futures.

Perhaps this needs clarification. Look at it this way: the future is not "there," waiting for time to uncover it. The future is as formless and colorless as a lump of clay. It is what we, all of us, will make of it. I wrote an optimistic book, but not because I think that is the way life will be in the future. I wrote it that way because that is the way we must make it be.

By showing what the future could be like, as in the Prologue, by showing that man need not be ignored or left out even in a "supermachine" age, I have tried to show what and how much still remains to be done. The fantastic promise of machines and computers can be, and must be, put to use for the comfort, aid, and use of the human. This is what new developments should be all about.

If we destroy our cities in an attempt to improve transportation, we shall be moving faster and faster, but from nowhere to nowhere.

In this book, we have considered a number of possible solutions to a difficult, complex, and nagging set of problems. Some of the solutions are complicated, others are expensive, most are impractical—now. But I dare anyone to point to a single approach and say, "It can't be done."

For example, a giant cargo container can now travel directly from a warehouse in Chicago to another in the heart of France without any layovers and without ever having to be unpacked. Once placed on the truck trailer, it can travel directly to dockside and be swung, as shown, right onto a ship (or plane). At the other end, it can be transferred to a train as well as a truck. The savings in time, effort, and expense are obvious.

This technique is known as *containerized shipping* and has been called "the greatest advance in freight movement since Railway Express." The point, of course, is that if this kind of "systemized" transportation can be accomplished for the transportation of goods, surely a way can be found to do it for humans, too.

One possible approach, the *traveling cartridge*, has been proposed by the brilliant and wide-ranging architect engineer,

Containerized Shipping

R. Buckminster Fuller. As you can see, the privacy and flexibility of the automobile is combined with the manifold possibilities and advantages of public transport. Clearly, however, there would be a considerable weight penalty in the extra motors, wheels, and car bodies that would have to be carried in the public transport modes. New developments in lightweight, super-strength materials might overcome this objection. A more persistent problem would be the difficulty in meshing the various aspects of such a many-sided system.

Perhaps aerospace management techniques for attacking large-scale problems and integrating large-scale operations can

174

be applied here on earth, as well as in building, launching, and tracking 6-million-pound rockets. Indeed, it may yet turn out that one of the greatest contributions of the aerospace industry will be the management and planning techniques that will make a reliable, flexible, and balanced transportation system a reality.

Concurrent with the development of these techniques has been the growth of computers which permit the storing, handling, and consideration of vast quantities of data. Myron

Fuller's Traveling Cartridge

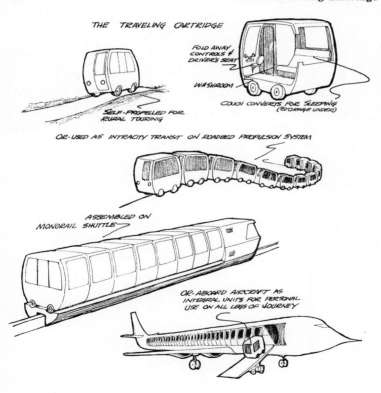

THE TRAVELING CARTRIDGE

FOLD AWAY CONTROLS & DRIVER'S SEAT

WASHROOM

COUCH CONVERTS FOR SLEEPING (STORAGE UNDER)

SELF-PROPELLED FOR RURAL TOURING

OR-USED AS INTRACITY TRANSIT ON ROADBED PROPULSION SYSTEM

ASSEMBLED ON MONORAIL SHUTTLE

OR-ABOARD AIRCRAFT AS INTEGRAL UNITS FOR PERSONAL USE ON ALL LEGS OF JOURNEY

175

Miller, Senior Engineer at the Office of High Speed Ground Transportation, says that the old ways of piecemeal planning are obsolete. More important, he points out, is the fact that with developments in computer engineering, new mathematical techniques, and the ability to make better trade-off and cost studies, we can for the first time begin to look at the larger problems. One example, of course, is the Northeast Corridor project.

Another hopeful sign is the $2.9 billion New York City transportation plan mentioned earlier. This is said to be the first time in the nation's history that a total regional approach has been taken to mass transportation, in which all modes of travel are being pulled together.

Included are plans for major improvements and extensions of subways and commuter trains, additional airports, and a giant transportation terminal in the heart of the city, as well as others in outlying districts. Included also are plans for a new midtown distribution system that would provide convenient passenger movement along the now-choked major cross-town thoroughfares: 34th, 42nd, 48th, and 57th Streets. This would involve moving sidewalks, small rail cars, or some other guided system which would link terminals, stores, offices, theaters, and other important CBD points.

It is an exciting prospect. For the first time, there is at least hope that the large-scale problem can be faced squarely and, perhaps, licked.

BIBLIOGRAPHY

BOOKS

Aerospace Industries Association of America, Inc., *Aerospace Facts and Figures • 1967*, Aero Publishers, Inc., 1967.

Blaisdell, R. F., et. al., *Sources of Information in Transportation*, Northwestern University Press, 1964.

Calder, Nigel, ed., *The World in 1984*, Penguin Books, 1965 (vols. 1 & 2).

Clarke, A. C., *Profiles of the Future*, Harper & Row, 1963.

Fabre, M., *A History of Land Transportation*, Hawthorn Books, Inc., 1963.

Firestone, H. S., Jr., *Man on the Move*, Putnam, 1967.

Furnas, C. C., *The Next Hundred Years*, Reynal & Hitchcock, 1936.

Gablehouse, Charles, *Helicopters and Autogiros*, Lippincott, 1967.

Gordon, T. J., *The Future*, St. Martin's Press, 1965.

Halacy, D. S., Jr., *Bionics, the Science of Living Machines*, Holiday House, 1965.

Hill, F. E., *The Automobile, How it Came, Grew and Changed our Lives*, Dodd, Mead, 1967.

Massachusetts Institute of Technology, *Project Metran: Boston 1990*, MIT Press, 1967.

Metcalf, K., ed., *Transportation Information Sources*, Gale Research Co., 1966.

Owen, Wilfred, *The Metropolitan Transportation Problem*, Doubleday, 1966.

Pell, Claiborn, *Megalopolis Unbound: The Supercity and Transportation of Tomorrow*, Praeger, 1966.

Port of New York Authority, Comprehensive Planning Office, *Metropolitan Transportation—1980*, 1963.

Richards, Brian, *New Movement in Cities*, Reinhold, 1966.

Ruppenthal, K. E., ed., *Transportation Frontiers*, Stanford University Graduate School of Business, 1962.

Ruppenthal, K. E., and H. A. McKinnell, Jr., eds., *Transportation and Tomorrow*, Stanford University Graduate School of Business, 1966.

Sandstrom, G. E., *Tunnels*, Holt, Rinehart and Winston, 1963.

Thomson, George, *The Foreseeable Future*, Cambridge University Press, 1955.

Wall Street Journal, *Here Comes Tomorrow*, Dow Jones Books, 1966, 1967.

BOOKLETS, REPORTS AND SYMPOSIUM PROCEEDINGS

Automobile Manufacturers Association, Inc. (320 New Center Building, Detroit, Michigan 48202), *1967 Automobile Facts and Figures.*

——, *Urban Transportation Issues and Trends*, June 1963.

Automotive Safety Foundation (200 Ring Building, Washington, D.C. 20036), *What Freeways Mean to Your City*, January 1964.

Commerce, U.S. Department of, *Surface Effect Ships for Ocean Commerce*, February 1966 (for sale by U.S. Government Printing Office).

Committee on Commerce and the Subcommittee on Air and Water Pollution of the Committee on Public Works (U.S. Senate), *Electric Vehicles and Other Alternatives to the Internal Combustion Engine, 1967* (U.S. Government Printing Office Yr.C 73/2: El 2).

Connecticut General Life Insurance Company (Bloomfield, Connecticut), *Aviation and the Transportation System: Progress, Profits and the Public Interest. Panel II, Aviation and Technological Progress: The Search for Better Ways,* February 1967.

Cornell Aeronautical Laboratory, Inc. (Cornell University, Buffalo, New York 14221) *Metrotran-2000—A Study of Future Concepts in Metropolitan Transportation for the Year 2000,* October 1967.

Health, Education and Welfare, U.S. Department of (National Center for Air Pollution Control, Cincinnati, Ohio), *Power Systems for Electric Vehicles* (proceedings of symposium held April 6-8, 1967).

Foa, J. V., *An Introduction to Project Tubeflight,* Rensselaer Polytechnic Institute, September 1966.

Haase, R. H., *Analysis of Some Land Transportation Vehicles—Today and Tomorrow,* Rand Corporation Report #P-2625, August 1962. (Santa Monica, California 90406)

Hall, E. N., *Central Elements of a National Transportation System,* United Aircraft Corporation Report, October 1967 (East Hartford, Connecticut 06108).

Hoffman, G. A., *On Minimizing the Land Used by Automobiles and Buses in the Urban Central Core:*

Underground Highways and Parking Facilities, Rand Corporation Report #P-3002, October 1964 Santa Monica, California 90406).

Housing and Urban Development, U.S. Department of, *Urban Public Transportation, Selected References* 1966 (U.S. Government Printing Office HUD MP-3).

Institute for Rapid Transit (Merchandise Mart, Chicago, Illinois 60654), *Selected Bibliography on Metropolitan Transportation and Planning,* May 1967.

Massachusetts Institute of Technology, *Survey of Technology for High Speed Ground Transport,* June 15, 1965 (Report #PB 168 648, distributed by Clearinghouse for Federal, Scientific and Technical Information).

Office of High Speed Ground Transportation (Department of Transportation, Washington, D.C. 20591), *Published Research Reports* (bibliography), June 16, 1967.

Port of New York Authority, *Container Shipping: Full Ahead,* May 1967.

Seifert, W. W., and R. J. Hansen, *Summary of Research at MIT on Technology for High-Speed Ground Transport, 16 September 1965 to 15 September 1966,* December 31, 1966 (Report # PB 173 658, distributed by Clearinghouse for Federal, Scientific and Technical Information).

Smith, Wilbur, and Associates (New Haven, Connecticut), *Parking in the City Center,* May 1965 (prepared for the Automobile Manufacturers Association, Inc., mentioned above).

———, *Transportation and Parking for Tomorrow's Cities,* 1966 (prepared for the Automobile Manufacturers Association, Inc.).

Stanford Research Institute (Menlo Park, California), *SRI Urban Transportation Alternatives Symposium* (proceedings of symposium held May 27, 1964).

Subcommittee on Department of Transportation, *Department of Transportation Appropriations for 1968* (hearings before a subcommittee of the Committee on Appropriations, House of Representatives), 1967.

Transportation Center Library, *Transportation of the Future: Selected References*, Northwestern University, 1967.

ARTICLES

Agle, C. K., "From Here to There: An Analysis and Proposal for Transit," *Traffic Quarterly*, April 1965.

Ash, David, "On a Clear Day You Will See the Electric Car," *New York Times Magazine*, January 29, 1967.

Asimov, Isaac, "Life in 1990, *Science Digest*, August 1965.

Avery, W. H., "Beyond the Supersonic Transport," *Science and Technology*, February 1968.

Barloon, M. J., "The Coming of the Super-Railroad," *Harper's Magazine*, April 1967.

Beller, W. S., "Megalopolis Transportation: Attacking the Systems Problem," *Space / Aeronautics*, September 1967.

Bouladon, G. "Transportation," *Science Journal*, October 1967 (published by Dorset House, Stamford St., London, S.E. 1, England).

Business Week, "Giants of the Ocean Grow Bigger Still (300,000 Ton Tankers Planned in Japan)," *Business Week*, April 16, 1966.

Butwin, D. W., "The Great Airport Dilemma," *Saturday Review*, January 6, 1968.

Butz, J. S., Jr., "Hypersonic Aircraft: Possible and Practical," *Air Force Magazine*, May 1965.

Carr, D. E., "The Case for the Electric Automobile," *Atlantic Monthly*, June 1967.

Chacey, D. K., "Ground Transportation in the Years Ahead," *Traffic Quarterly*, April 1964.

Christie, T. L. "The Once and Future Ships," *Saturday Review*, January 6, 1968.

Clarke, Evert, "Up in the Clouds with the SST," *Saturday Review*, January 6, 1968.

Copeland, E., Jr., "Air-Cushion Craft," *Ordnance*, May-June, 1965.

Cote, A. J., Jr., "Electronics in Transportation," *Industrial Research*, July 1967.

Dulberger, L. H., "Advanced Rotary Wing Aircraft," *Space/Aeronautics*, April 1967.

Dyckman, J. W., "Transportation in Cities," *Scientific American*, September 1965.

Edwards, L. K., "High Speed Tube Transportation," *Scientific American*, August 1965.

Evans, G. G., and K. V. Kordesch, "Hydrazine-Air Fuel Cells," *Science*, 1 December 1967.

Ewan, T. K., "Supersonic Combustion for Sustained Hypersonic Flight," *Naval Engineer's Journal*, August 1967.

Friedlander, G. D., "Railway vs. Highway—the Zoom of Things to Come," *IEEE Spectrum*, September 1967.

Gilmore, C. P., "Electric Autos—They're on the Way," *Popular Science*, December 1966.

——, "How You'll Drive the Amazing Urbmobile," *Popular Science*, October 1967.

Hanson, R. J., "High Speed Ground Transportation," *Journal of the Boston Society of Civil Engineers*, October 1966.

Hawkins, W. M., "The Next 50 Years in Aviation," *Astronautics & Aeronautics*, July 1965.

Herbert, Evan, "Transporting People," *International Science & Technology*, October 1965.

Howard, T. E., "Rapid Excavation," *Scientific American*, November 1967.

Industrial Research, "Steam Engine Car Awaits Demand," *Industrial Research*, September 1967.

International Railway Journal, "Monorails: Where Do They Stand Today," *International Railway Journal*, March 1965.

Jones, P. S., "Moving Things," *Science & Technology*, February 1968.

Keeping, G. K., "Design in Transportation," *Industrial Research*, July 1967.

Kent, J. L., "Wild New Flying Machines," *Science Digest*, February 1967.

Kucher, A. J., "The Levacar," *High Speed Ground Transportation Journal*, January 1967.

Leary, Frank, "High-Speed Ground Transportation," *Space / Aeronautics*, September 1967.

Leedham, Charles, "The Handwriting on the Air Terminal Wall," *New York Times Magazine*, May 21, 1967.

Levin, S. M., and M. P. London, "Aircraft for the Short Haul," *Space / Aeronautics*, September 1967.

Life Magazine, "Master Modemixer," *Life Magazine*, December 24, 1965.

McLean, W. B., "Future Exploration of the Ocean," *Astronautics and Aeronautics*, July 1966.

Mackenzie, A. T., "Marine Automation—Future Developments?" *Shipping World*, January 19, 1967.

Mecklin, John, "The $4-Billion Machine That Reshapes Geography," (the SST), *Fortune*, February 1967.

Packer, R. E., "The Automated Processing of People," *Computers and Automation*, April 1966.

Product Engineering, "Supermagnetism Supports a Train at Airliner Speed," *Product Engineering*, January 16, 1967.

Reba, Imants, "Mass Transport for the Future," *Frontiers*, Spring 1967 (Illinois Institute of Technology).

Ritter, Norman, "Interstate 87," *Atlantic Monthly*, September 1967.

Ronan, W. J., "New Approach to Metropolitan Transportation," *Going Places*, Second Quarter 1967, (General Electric).

Semenov, N. N., "The World of the Future," *Bulletin of the Atomic Scientists*, February 1964.

Siekman, Philip, "The Big New Whirl in Helicopters," *Fortune*, April 1966.

Sinclair, P. M., "Materials in Transportation," *Industrial Research*, July 1967.

Space / Aeronautics, "Transportation," *Space / Aeronautics*, January 1968.

Stambler, Irwin, "Systems Analysis in Transportation," *Industrial Research*, July 1967.

Sutton, Horace, "Tomorrow's Traveler," *Saturday Review*, January 6, 1968.

Bibliography

Teale, E. L. and L. P. Adair, "Nuclear Powers: the Marine Industry is Ready and Capable to Proceed," *Marine Engineering Log*, March 1966.

Thomas, B. K., Jr., "New Wing Design Promises Design Breakthrough," *Aviation Week & Space Technology*, July 24, 1967.

U.S. News and World Report, "The Wondrous World of 1990: Outlook for Young People," *U.S. News and World Report*, January 30, 1967.

Von Eckardt, W., "Redesigning American Airports," *Harper's Magazine*, March 1967.

Walordy, Alex, "Underground in Montreal," *Science & Mechanics*, September 1967.

Yaffee, M. L., "NASA Engine Work Keyed to Components," *Aviation Week & Space Technology*, September 4, 1967.

INDEX

Acceleration factors, 24, 26-27, 47, 58, 66, 70. *See also* Speed
"Acceleration lanes," 81
Acoustical holography, 144
ACV (Air-Cushion Vehicle), 24, 51-53, 55, 135-37
ADAM (Air Deflection and Modulation), 160
Aerial Transport System, 33-35
Aerodynamic lifting surfaces, 51
Aerostatic lift vehicles, 134
Aerotrain, 51-53
Air bearings, 51
Air Bus, 164
Air Conditioners, 61
Air cushions: ACV, 24, 51-53, 55, 135-38; and boat travel, 134-38
Air Gulper, the, 63, 65
Air jets, whirling, 63-64
Air pads, 51, 52
Air pollution, 57, 61, 62, 90-91,125; and electric cars, 92-99
Air pressure, 52, 60, 61ff., 72
Air resistance, 61, 64, 65-68, 72
AiResearch Corporation, 58
Airfoils, 49, 134
Airplanes (air transportation), 60, 146-71 (*See also* specific kinds, problems, etc.); and travel time, 42-43, 146-71; vs. railroads, 22, 40, 41, 42-43; and weather, 43
Airports, 148, 151
Alden StaRRcar, 122, 124, 127
Altman, Manfred, 99
Apollo Command Module, 98, 102
Autoline, 86
Automatic expressways, 3-4, 19, 27-32, 82-89
Automation, experiments in, 27-32, 34, 118-28. *See also* specific problems, systems
Automobile Manufacturer's Association, 80, 94
Automobiles, 11, 14, 15, 16, 27, 42, 47, 60, 76-91 (*See also* Roads); and automatic highways, 3-4, 27-32, 82-89; electric, 92-99; and rapid

transit systems, 36-37, 47; road/rail systems, 112-28; vs. trains, 18, 21, 41, 42, 47

Baltimore, Md., 12, 78
BART, 31, 32
Battery systems, 97-99
Bay Area Rapid Transit (BART), San Francisco, 31, 32
Bell Aerosystems Co., 101-2, 135, 156, 159
Belts, moving, 106
Beltway plan, 78
Bensen Gyrocopter, 105
Berkeley, Calif., 31
Berri-de Montigny station, 27
Bertin Aerotrain, 51-53
Boats, transportation by, 129-45
Boeing *707*, 167
Boeing *747*, 163
Bonneville Salt Flats, 68
Booz, Allen Applied Research, Inc., 135
Boron filament fibers, 158
"Bosnywash," 12
Boston, Mass., 11, 12, 21, 47, 78
Braking, 49, 50, 52-53, 58, 66, 84
Bridwell, Lowell, 86
Bronx River Parkway, 81
Brookhaven National Laboratory, 55
Brooklyn, N.Y., 31-32
Brussels (Belgium) subway, 42
Budd Company, 47
Buses, 16, 21, 42; electric, 105; rail-bus systems, 118-28

Capsules: electrically driven, 90; passenger-carrying, 116
Carr, Donald E., 96
Carveyor circuit, 109-11
CBD. *See* Central Business District
Celestial Research Inc., 64
Central Business District (CBD), 11, 14, 15, 16, 31, 35, 36; and automatic passenger processing, 105-11; and underground highways, 90; and VTOL service, 151

Central Control, 29
Century Expressway, 87
Channel tunnel, 113-14
Chemicals, use in tunneling, 74
Chicago, Ill., 11, 12, 36, 87
"Chipitt," 12
Cities: bypassing 78-91; electric cars and air pollution, 92-101; modern megalopolis, 11-14; problems of transportation, 14; rail rapid transit and, 20-37; transportation and, 8-19
Cleveland, Ohio, 42
Coaches, 38
Coils, superconducting, 55-57
Comfort: and boat transportation, 130; and train travel, 11, 38, 39-40, 45, 62
Commercial submarines, 140-45
Communications, 9, 31, 89, 105
Commuters (commuting), 10-11, 12, 15, 16, 18 (*See also* specific problems, systems); and electric cars, 101; and rail rapid transit, 20-37, 40-58 *passim*
Compound helicopters, 155-56
Computers, 26, 30-31, 173, 175-76; and automated highways, 87-89
Concorde, the, 166
Congestion problems, 14, 15, 22, 35, 125 (*See also* specific systems); and air travel, 149, 151; and electric cars, 101; and roads ahead, 76-91
Congress, U.S., 17, 41, 45, 75
Congress Street Expressway, 87
Congressional, the (train), 43
Containerized shipping, 173
Control system, automated highway, 82-91
Convenience factors, 82, 96
Cornell Aeronautical Laboratory, 87, 122, 150
Corridor, the. *See* Northeast Corridor
Costs. *See* Expenditures
Cross traffic, 105-6
Cummings, J. J., 80
Cunard Steamship Co., 163
Curves; carveyor, 109-10; railroad, 49, 62
Cushions, air: ACV, 24, 51-53, 55, 135-38, 143; and boat travel, 134-38, 143
"Cyrogenic" temperatures, 55

Dallas, Texas, City Council, 90
Danby, G. T., 55
Dep't of Transportation Act, 17
Detroit, Mich., 14, 87
Diamonds, 72
Dickens, Charles, 131
Diesel engines, 24
Dimethylhydrazine, 102
Disneyland, 108
Disney World, 108
Dolphins, 143
Douglas Aircraft Co., 144
Downtowner (X-142A), 159
Doxiados, Constantinos, 75, 89
Drag, 62, 65, 133
Duo-rails, 33
"Dynamic instabilities," 50

Edwards, L. K., 65, 66, 67-69, 73
Ejection of whirling air jets propulsion method, 64
Ele-Car, 5
Electric buses, 105
Electric cars, 92-101, 122
Electric currents, and magnetic suspension, 55-57
Electric motors ("linear motors"), 57-58
Electric power, third-rail, 24, 49, 62
Electrification: of rail transportation, 46, 66, 75; of trolley systems, 21
Electronic highways, 3-4, 19, 27-32, 82-89
Electronic sensors, 88
"Elevated," the, 10
Energy (*See also* specific kinds): high-frequency, 62-63; as key to technological future, 75, 97ff.
Engines, 24, 61-62; and high-speed ground transportation, 38-58 *passim*; nuclear, 98, 140-43; turbine, 24, 48-49, 62, 97, 154; and underground transportation, 59-75 *passim*
England, 39-40, 53, 93, 113-14, 135
English Channel tunnel, 113-14, 135
Escalators, 107-8
Evaporation and propulsion, 64-65
Expenditures: and air travel, 149, 163; income and transportation, 9, 14; Interstate Highway System, 16; and rail rapid transit, 23-24, 27-28, 30, 32, 41, 42, 62; and tunneling, 75
Expressway, 27 (*See also* Highways;

Roads); around cities, 78-81; automatic, 3-4, 19, 27-32, 86
Fatalities, 60. *See also* Safety factors
Fan-in-wing VTOL, 160
Federal Aviation Agency, 17
Federal Highway Adm'n, 86, 89
Flame jets, 73
Flexible sign system, 88
Flery, L. E., 84
Fluid suspension, 51
Flying submarines, 145
Foa, J. V., 61-62, 63, 65
Foils, boat, 130-33, 134, 139-40
Ford Motor Co., 97, 164
Freeways, 17, 80-81. *See also* Expressways; Roads
Freight. *See* Goods, transportation of
Fuel cells, 98-99
Fuller, R. Buckminster, 174
Fumes. *See* Air pollution

Gapmeasuring, 88
Gases, and magnetic propulsion, 63
Gases, and VTOL's, 160
Gasoline-powered cars vs. electric cars, 93-97, 98
Gemini space flights, 98
"Gems" (ground effect machines), 137, 138
General Dynamics/Convair, 145
General Electric Co., 33, 98
General Motors Corp., 53, 58, 85-86
Goods, transportation of, 8, 9, 14, 15, 44; containerized shipping, 173; underwater, 140-45
Goodyear People Mover, 108
Government, 17-18, 46, 74
Graphite, 72
Gravity, 27, 49, 69-70, 102
Gravity-vacuum system, 65, 116
Great Lakes area, 12
Ground effect machines ("gems"), 137, 138
Ground transportation, high-speed, 38-58
Guidance, highway, 82-89
Guideways, 53, 55, 60, 62, 122-28
Gyrocopters, 105

Hall, Edward M., 127
Hanson, R. J., 50
Harben, William, 146-47
HDL. *See* Hovercar
Headways, 27, 28, 30

Heat, 61, 72, 73. *See also* Temperatures
Helicopters, 89, 102, 148-60
Heinlein, Robert, 106
Helium, liquid, 57
High-frequency energy, 62-63
High Speed Ground Transportation Act, 45, 50, 63, 75
Highways, 15 (*See also* Expressways; Roads); automating, 3-4, 82-89; underground, 89-91
Hikari (lightning) trains, 44
Hoffman, George A., 89-90
Holography, 144
Housing, 31-32
Housing and Urban Affairs, Department of, 17
Hovair, 53, 58
Hovercar, 53, 58
Hovercraft, 137, 138
Hovercraft Development, Ltd., 53, 58
HST (hypersonic transport), 168
Hughes Heavy-Lifter, 149
Hughes Tool Company, 156
Hydrazine, 102
Hydrazine-air fuel cells, 98
Hydrocarbons, 91, 98
Hydrofoils, 130-33, 134, 139-40, 143
Hypersonic aircraft, 168-71

ICC. *See* Interstate Commerce Commission
In-motion transfers, 116-18
"In the Year Ten Thousand," 146-47
India, 11
Inertial navigation, 144
Integrated public transportation, 4, 7, 24, 42
Intersections, eliminating, 81
Interstate Commerce Commission, 40
Interstate Highway System, 16
Intracity travel, Housing and Urban Affairs Dept., 17

Jacksonville, Fla., 114, 115
Japan, 44, 68, 145
Jet aircraft, 40, 61-62, 160-71
Jet engines, 61-62
Jet-belts, 101-2
Jet skimmers, 135
Jones, John, 140

Kennedy International Airport, 42, 121, 148

184

Kettering, Charles, 115
Kodama (echo) trains, 44
Koyoto, Japan, 44

LaGuardia Airport, 12-14, 148
Laminar flow, 143
Lane-changers, 88
Lasers, 51, 73, 144
Large-clearance fluid suspension, 62
Lenin (ship), 140
Lift (lifting power), 151, 155
"Linear City," 31-32
Linear motors, 57-58, 62
Ling-Temco-Vought, 159
Lightweight train bodies, 49
Lockheed C-5A, 161
Lockheed L-500, 161
Locomotive 999, 39
London, England, 10, 77
Long Island, N.Y., 23-24, 42, 81, 121;
    Expressway, 81; Rail Road, 23-24,
    42, 121
Loops, 35; electrical, 57, 110
Los Angeles, Calif., 11, 14, 16-17
Los Angeles Airways, 151
Low, A. M., 10

McLean, Robert F., 120
McNay, David E., 143
Magnetic suspension, 55-57
Magnetogasdynamics, 63-64
Mann, Andrew, 3-6, 7, 106
Manhattan, 11, 12, 20, 121 (*See also*
    New York City); and air travel,
    147-51; and L.I.R.R., 24; proposed
    highway across, 75, 78-79
Mass transit, 16, 20-37 (*See also*
    specific aspects, problems, sys-
    tems); regional approach, 12, 176
Massachusetts Inst. of Tech., 50
Master Mode-Mixer, 150
Materials technology, 32, 143, 158,
    170
Mechanical contact suspension, 50
Megalopolis, 11-14, 21
Melpar, Inc., 47
Merging, vehicular, 88
Metropolitan Transportation Author-
    ity, New York, 23-25, 121
Michigan State University, 87
Microwave energy, 62-63
Miller, Myron, 175-76
Miller, René, 168
Minibus, 105

Missiles, 145
Monitoring, and control of express-
    ways, 87, 88
Monorails, 33-35, 42
Montreal Metro, 25-27, 30
Moon, use of Pogo on, 102
Motion, laws of, 61, 138

Nagoya, Japan, 44
National transportation policies, 17
Nautilus (submarine), 144
Navigation problems, 144
New Brunswick, N.J., 46
New Haven, Conn., 12
New Jersey turnpike, 78
New York Airways, 149
New York City (*See also* Manhat-
    tan): and air travel, 147-51; con-
    gestion and move to suburbs, 9-10;
    metropolitan megalopolis, 11-13;
    and rail rapid transit, 20, 21, 23-
    25, 31-32, 42, 43, 47
New York State (*See also* New York
    City): and rail rapid transit, 23-24
Newark Airport, 148
Newton's laws of motion, 61, 138
Niobium-titanium wire, 55
Nitrogen tetroxide, 102
Noise, 25-26, 57, 77
North American Aviation Co., 143
Northeast Corridor, 12, 44, 45, 47-48,
    66, 176; multi-use transportation
    and utility tunnel, 75
Nuclear-powered aircraft, 165
Nuclear-powered car, 98
Nuclear-powered ships, 140-43, 144,
    145

Oakland, Calif., 31
Obstructions, roadway, 89, 90
Ocean travel, 129-45
Osaka, Japan, 44
Otto Hahn (ship), 140
Owen, Wilfred, 12

Packer, R. E., 37
Pallet-type systems, 127, 128
Pan Am Building Heliport, 149
Park-and-ride stations, 47
Parking problems, 14, 16, 90
Passenger trains, disappearance of,
    40-41
Passengers (*See also* specific modes
    of transportation): automatic

processing of, 107-11; capsules carrying, 116-20
Pelee Island, 137
Pendulous suspension, 49, 62
Penn Central Railroad, 41, 45-46, 47
Penn Station (NYC), 24
PeopleMover, 108, 109, 127
Petroleum products, 74
Philadelphia, Pa., 11, 12, 47
Photochromic glass, 101
"Piggy-back" trains, 19, 112, 114, 116, 128
"Piston" characteristic, 65
Pittsburgh, Pa., 12, 29
Pneumatic systems, 24, 66-67, 69-70
Pods, 117, 128, 151
Pogo, the, 102
Population, 10, 11-14, 15-16, 22, 23, 35-37, 45, 75
Port of New York Authority, 121
Powell, J. R., 55
Power (See also Energy; specific kinds): new sources of, 97-99
Pressure, air, 52, 60, 61ff., 72
Project Tubeflight, 62
Propellers, 51, 57, 64
Propulsion systems, 50, 51, 57, 61-75 (See also specific problems, systems); and boat travel, 129-45; new ideas in, 63-68
Providence, R. I., 12
Public Roads, Bureau of, 17
Pullman, Standard, 48

Queen of Bermuda (ship), 142
Queen Elizabeth (ship), 163
Queen Elizabeth II (ship), 163
Queen Mary (ship), 133, 141

Radio Corporation of America, 84
Railbuses, 118-28
Railroads, 18-19, 20-37 (See also specific systems); development of, 20-37, 38-58; and high-speed ground transportation, 39-58; problems, 40-46 (See also specific problems); and rapid transit, 20-37; road/rail systems, 112-28; underground, 60-75
Rails, 22, 46, 68
"Ram effect," 52
Ramjets, 169-70
Rapid transit, 10, 11, 20-37. (See also specific systems)

Reactors, nuclear, 98, 144
Regional Plan Ass'n, 12, 176
Remote control lane-changers, 88
Research, 18, 45ff., 74. (See also specific problems, systems)
Rights-of-way, railroad, 21, 22
Rensselaer Polytech. Inst., 61
Roads, 15-16, 76-91 (See also Automobiles; Expressways; Highways); automating, 27-32, 82-89; and rail systems, 112-28; underground, 89
"Roads Must Roll, The," 106
Robotugs, 106
Rock, tunneling through, 73-74
Rockets, 57, 147, 175
Rolling members, 50
Romans, ancient, 73, 77
Romualdi, James P., 99
Ronan, William C., 23-25, 68
Rotors, 154-57, 159
Route 128 (Boston), 78
RRollway, 115
Rubber tires, 25-26, 68
Rubber wheels, 26, 33
Russia, 135

SAFEGE, 33
Safety factors, 15, 49, 60, 82
San Diego, Calif., 12, 78
San Francisco, Calif., 12, 30-31
"Sansan," 12
Saunders, Stuart, 46
Savannah (ship), 140
Scramjets, 169
Seattle, Wash., 129-30
Seifert, W. W., 50
SES, 133-34
Ships. See Boats
Sidewalks, moving, 106
Sikorsky Flying Crane, 151
Silver-zinc battery, 97
Single-track systems, 35
SK-5's, 135
Skybus program, 151
Slopes, tunnel, 69-70, 73
Sodium-sulphur battery, 97-98
Sonar, 144
Sonic boom, 167-68
Space, highway, 82-83, 84
Speed, 15, 30. (See also Acceleration factors; Propulsion systems; Trip time; specific problems, systems)
Speedwalk passenger conveyer, 106
Spilhaus, Athelstan, 144

SRN-4, 135
SST, 165-68
Stanford Res. Inst., 40, 41
StaRRcar, 122, 124, 127
Steam power, 38, 39
Steel wheels, 26, 49, 68, 116
Stephens-Adamson Mfg. Co., 109
Stockholm, Sweden, 32
STOL's, 151
Stowed-rotor design, 156
Streamlining, 49, 61, 66
Streetcars, 10, 21
Submarines, 140-45
Subsonic mode, 167-68
Subways, 10, 15, 24, 25-27, 34, 67;
   Brussels, 42
Supersonic aircraft, 160, 165-71
Surface effect ship, 133-34
Suspension, 35, 50-51, 55 (*See also*
   specific systems); for high-speed
   vehicles, 50-51, 55; underground,
   61-75

Tampa Airport, 29
Technology, 18-19, 46-58 (*See also*
   specific aspects, problems, systems);
   materials, 32, 143, 158, 170
Television monitoring, 87
Temperatures, 55-57, 61, 72, 168, 170
Test trains, 46-48
Thermonuclear fusion engines, 144
Third-rail power, 24, 49, 62
Thrust, 61, 155
Tilt-Rotor, 156
Titanium, 168
Tokyo, Japan, 33, 42, 44
Track conditions, 46, 49
Tracks, rapid transit, 24, 33, 34-35,
   52
Transfers, in-motion, 116-18
Transit, 20-37, 38-58
Transit Expressway, 28-29
Transportation Dept., 17-18, 58, 114
Travel time. *See* Trip time
Traveling cartridge, 173-74
Trenton, N. J., 46
Trip time, 40, 42-43ff., 60, 70-73
Tubeflight, 62, 65
Tubes, 59-68

Tufts University, 61
Tunnels, 49, 57, 59-75, 89-91, 112-14
Turbine engines, 24, 48, 62, 97, 154
Turbo-prop engines, 60
Turbo-Train, 48, 62

Udall, Stewart, 101
Unconventional systems, 50-58
Underground transportation, 59-75, 89-
   91, 140-45
United Aircraft, 48, 62
United Air Lines, 106
Uranium, 98
Urban areas, 10-19 (*See also* Cities);
   and rail rapid transit, 20-37
Urban Beautification Demonstration
   grants, 32
Urbmobile, 122-28

Vaccum, creation of, 65
Vapor, saturated, 64-65
Verne, Jules, 140
Vertical guidance, 53
Vertical take-off and landing, 151-60
Victoria, H.M.S., 129-30
V/STOL's, 151
VTOL's, 151-60

Wall Street Heliport, 149
Washington, D.C., 12, 31, 42, 43, 76,
   114; beltway around, 78
Water jets, 74
Watercraft 129-45, 163
Waveguides, 63
Waves, 131-33, 141-42
Weather, 43, 59-60, 141
Weiland airfoil, 134
Western Pacific Railroad, 40-41
Westinghouse Electric, 28, 31, 127
Wheels, 26, 33, 49, 50
Wright brothers, 146
Wuppertal monorail, 33

X-15, 168-69
X-22A, 159
X-142A, 159
XV-5A, 160

Zephyr, 41

PICTURE CREDITS

PAGE

Title page	Cornell Aeronautical Laboratory
25	General Electric
26	Montreal Transportation Commission
28	Westinghouse Electric Corp.
29	Westinghouse Electric Corp.
30	San Francisco Bay Area Transit District
31	General Electric
36	General Electric
45	Japanese National Railways
48	United Aircraft Corporation
52	Aeroglide Systems, Inc.
54	Space/Aeronautics Magazine
56	Product Engineering
64	J. V. Foa
67	Tube Transit Corp.
74	Perkin-Elmer
79	Chicago Area Transportation Study
83	Ford Motor Company
85	General Motors
86	Ford Motor Company
95	Ford Motor Company
96	West Penn Power Company
100	General Electric
103	Bell Aerosystems Company
104	Bensen Aircraft Corp.
107	Space/Aeronautics Magazine
110	American City Magazine
119	General Motors
121	Port of New York Authority
123	Alden Self-Transit System Corporation
125	Cornell Aeronautical Laboratory
126	Westinghouse Electric Corp.
131	Northwest Hydrofoil Lines
132	Grumman Aircraft Engineering Corp.
136	United Press International
139	Bell Aerosystems Company
142	Lockheed Aircraft Corp.
152-53	Cornell Aeronautical Laboratory
155	Lockheed Aircraft Corp.
157 UPPER	Ling-Temco-Vought
157 LOWER	Bell Aerosystems Company
158	Ling-Temco-Vought
160	Lockheed Aircraft Corp.
164	Ford Motor Company
162	Lockheed Aircraft Corp.
166	The Boeing Company
169	Lockheed Aircraft Corp.
170	General Electric
174	Port of New York Authority
175	Think